Finite Sets:
Theory, Counting,
and Applications

Laurence P. Maher, Jr.
North Texas State University

Finite Sets: Theory, Counting, and Applications

Charles E. Merrill Publishing Company
Columbus, Ohio

A Bell & Howell Company

Merrill's
Mathematics and Quantitative Methods
Series

under the editorship of
Vincent E. Cangelosi
and
Melvin J. Hinich

Library of Congress Catalog Card Number: 68-19057

Printed in the United States of America
1 2 3 4 5 6 7 8 9 10 11 12 13 14 15 76 75 74 73 72 71 70 69 68

to self-reliant thinkers everywhere:
people who, though they may not always
succeed at sorting logic from illogic,
nevertheless recognize that no one *else*
should perform this service for them

Editors' Preface

This series is a new approach to the ever growing problem of providing appropriate material for basic mathematics courses offered for those planning careers in fields other than mathematics. Rapidly changing concepts in what should be offered at the undergraduate level have led to many approaches with various arrangements of topics. A serious problem arises in an effort to implement all of the material needed to satisfy the needs of these different courses. Too often there is no single book that treats the material in the desired manner or includes the desired topics at an acceptable level.

This series is planned as an integrated group of high quality books, each complete within itself except for required background material, each covering a specified topic, and each preparing the reader for the topics that would follow naturally.

With the flexibility that such a series offers, it is hoped that every requirement can be satisfied by a careful selection of books. In designing the series, we have tried to meet two requirements. We have tried, first, to satisfy the need for flexibility in the subject material; and secondly, to present to the reader material that has been prepared by an author with a specialized background in that particular area.

In editing this series, we have insisted that each author treat his subject material in a way to give it operational meaning. With the specialist's greater familiarity in a particular subject, he can delicately merge the abstract with the practical. He can give a functional interpretation to the concepts of mathematics, thereby motivating the student and creating the necessary interest to make the learning experience exciting.

We owe a deep debt of gratitude to each author who has contributed to the series. Further, we are grateful to Charles E. Merrill Publishing

Company for the assistance they have given us in the development of this series.

Austin, Texas   Vincent E. Cangelosi
Pittsburgh, Pennsylvania   Melvin J. Hinich

Author's Preface

The two major aims of this book are, first, to give the reader a thorough understanding of the nature of the things under discussion so that he can reason about them and be self-reliant in using them (and will not simply have a superficial understanding, to be used for formal problem-solving or the passing of exams), and, second, to illustrate applications to everyday life by giving a wide variety of examples and problems.

I have written with a deliberate informality, in order to make this book easier reading for those who have had no previous exposure to the subject matter; and I have tried to present the material in such a way that, if necessary, this book can be used without supplementary aid from an instructor. It is usable either as a classroom textbook, as a supplement to a classroom textbook, or as a source of information for the interested layman.

The entire first chapter is devoted to the nature of the *set* notion and other primitive notions which accompany it. This is in sharp contrast to other books on set theory, which usually introduce *set* with only a line or two and assume the reader is able to distinguish between things that are sets and things that are not sets. Here, however, the foundations of thought about finite sets, primitive notions, and models are explored, and the reader is introduced to the common errors and pitfalls. Meaningful use of the English language is stressed, and examples of self-deception are given.

The nature of axioms is explained in Chapter 3 and the finite-probability-space axioms are stated. What they do and do not say is considered at length, and several examples satisfying some or all of them are given. A sequence of theorems is stated, very careful proofs are given for a few, and the reader is asked to prove the other theorems. Boolean algebra is then introduced.

Chapter 4 begins by explaining how a finite probability space is constructed as a model each time a probability problem is encountered in the physical world. The need for the counting of finite sets naturally follows this. There is a lengthy development of permutations, combinations, the binomial theorem, the binomial and hypergeometric probability laws, and some occupancy problems. The usual binomial-coefficient identities are given as theorems to be proved by the reader. They are then related to Pascal's Triangle.

One feature which I feel is highly desirable is that, instead of introducing an empty set as a primitive notion, this book uses an axiom to introduce a set $\emptyset$ which is a subset of every set in the probability space. The two alternatives yield equivalent mathematical results, but the latter does not require $\emptyset$ to be memberless. This pleases people for whom empty sets lack appeal. Of course, null-setters may consider my $\emptyset$ memberless if they choose.

At the end of each chapter are some problems which give the reader practice and require only superficial understanding, but there are also many problems which demand careful understanding of the nature of the things the text deals with, plus self-reliance in reasoning about them. The problems have much variety of subject and also of difficulty.

I would like to acknowledge my gratitude to the editors of this series, Professor Vincent Cangelosi and Professor Melvin Hinich, for their very kind assistance and suggestions. I am also very grateful to my wife, Mary, for her kind encouragement and excellent stenography.

Laurence P. Maher, Jr.

Contents

Finite Sets:
Theory, Counting,
and Applications

chapter one

Some Basic Properties of Sets

I challenge you to define one of the words *chance, between, thing, such, if, set, event, straight* or *the*. Do not merely thumb through a dictionary for a more complicated word with the same or opposite meaning—rather search your mind for more basic words with plainer meanings. Confine yourself to the English language. (Feel free to wave your hands.) A few minutes of this labor may lead you to suspect (and a dictionary will convince you) that there are some words for notions which are so fundamental that we should not and need not define them in terms of other English words. Indeed, it is illogical to attempt a definition for each word in a language because each word would be indirectly defined in terms of itself. Problem 1–1 illustrates this point. Since we must begin by accepting some words as undefined, we should let these be the words for the most basic or primitive notions and make all definitions in terms of them.*

---

*The initial volume of the Mathematics and Quantitative Methods Series addresses itself to this question in some detail in Chapter 5. (See Vincent E. Cangelosi, *Compound Statements and Mathematical Logic* [Columbus, Ohio: Charles E. Merrill Publishing Company, 1967].)

1–1. THE NOTION OF A SET

Set and *member* are two of these very primitive notions. We begin by taking them as undefined; later we shall add other words to our list of undefined terms. If your native tongue is English, you have probably talked about sets of things and members of sets since early youth: sets of dishes, sets of chairs, members of a club. Unfortunately, laymen may add to the word *set* some shades of meaning which the mathematician wants to avoid. A gunsmith, for example, might say that two pistols do not form a set unless they are matching pistols, but we mathematicians (you and I) will not require members of a set to be alike or related in any way. To us, Winston Churchill and Adolph Hitler form a two-member set, and if this shocks you, consider the fact that Bach, Beethoven, Brahms and Al Capone also form a set. (That is, these would be sets if all these men were alive.) In fact, we shall even allow ourselves to consider such unrelated things as three elephants, California, and the jack of hearts as forming a set.

Another shade of meaning which is sometimes attached to the word *set*, and which we shall avoid, is that of a housewife who owns only two dinner plates and only twenty saucers, but no other dishes. She would claim (vigorously) that she does not possess a set of dishes, because she has not enough pieces and not enough variety, but we do not want to attach her requirements to our notions of *set*. For our purposes the notion of a set of dishes or a set of tools assumes nothing about the variety of the members or the wisdom or completeness of selection. The word *collection* is also commonly used for the primitive notion we are discussing, and we will let *set* and *collection* have the same meaning. Moreover, we will let the word *element* mean the same as the word *member*, so that we may talk about a *member of a collection* or an *element of a set* or an *element of a collection* and understand each to mean *member of a set*. Despite the fact that the word "collection" comes from the word "collect," we shall not require the members of a collection to be together. We shall consider the islands of Japan and the British Isles as forming an island collection even though they are separated by the globe.

A political party is an example of a set whose members are people, if some clear criterion for membership is agreed upon. The collection of all current American political parties is another example of a set. This is a set of sets. A graph is an example of a point set and so is a surface. A collection of counting numbers is an example of a number set. Note that there are many collections of counting numbers, but there is only one collection of *all* counting numbers. There is a set such that a thing is a member of it if and only if that thing is either the Eiffel Tower or is a coin which was in your pocket yesterday. The set such that x is a member of it if and only if x is you, is an example of a set with only one member—namely you.

We now come to the question of what we should mean by the statement that the set A is the same as the set B. The primitive notion we have in mind is such that a set A is the same as a set B if and only if each member of A is a member of B and each member of B is a member of A. Under these conditions we say that A is B, which means that A and B are two names for the same thing. If all this seems obvious, consider the example of a social club whose financial committee has all the members of the entertainment committee on it and whose entertainment committee has all the members of the financial committee on it. Is the financial committee the same as the entertainment committee? If we want to consider a committee as a set of people, then we must say that the financial committee is the same as the entertainment committee—two names for the same set —because the membership of one committee is the same as the membership of the other.

1–2. REASONS FOR STUDYING SETS

The world of mathematics is an abstract world of logic which exists entirely in the mind. For instance, mathematical things such as numbers and "perfectly straight" lines are products of our minds and cannot be seen, touched, heard, or eaten for breakfast, as we can often do with the things of the material world outside our minds. Nevertheless, mathematical things can be highly useful for solving important problems encountered in the material world. To solve such problems mathematically we always construct in our imagination some mathematical idea which is a model of the situation in the material world. Then we reason about our model. For example, suppose a man in Austin knows that the distance from Dallas is about 200 miles and the distance from Houston is about 150 miles, but he wants to know the distance between Dallas and Houston. If he notices on a globe or map that the three cities remind him of a right triangle with its right angle "at Austin," he can solve his problem. Figure 1–1a. illustrates the situation. The mathematical model he imagines is a right triangle with legs of lengths 200 and 150, like the model in Figure 1–1b. He applies reasoning to his model: he knows the sum of the squares of the legs of a right triangle equals the square of the hypotenuse, according to the Theorem of Pythagoras. Since $(200)^2 + (150)^2 = (250)^2$, the hypotenuse of his model triangle must have length 250. Under the assumption that his idea is a "good" model for the situation, the man decides

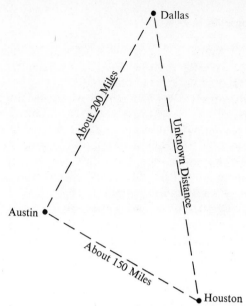

FIGURE 1-1a. Dallas, Austin and Houston, Which Are Three Cities in the Material World, Remind Us of a Right Triangle.

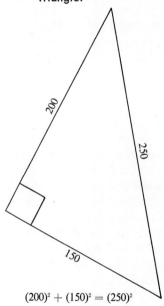

$$(200)^2 + (150)^2 = (250)^2$$

FIGURE 1-1b. A Mathematical Model Which Is Imagined in Order to Find the Unknown Distance.

4

that the distance from Dallas to Houston is about 250 miles. This example illustrates how a model obtained from plane geometry can indicate a solution to a problem in the material world. The appropriateness of the answer depends entirely upòn how closely the model "fits" the conditions of the problem.

Set theory is another field of mathematics which is often used in constructing mathematical models for the purpose of problem solving. The probability problem, for example, is a very important kind of material-world problem which always requires some set theory (often in combination with other mathematical fields such as plane geometry) for the construction of models. A probability problem is one in which there is some "chance situation" or "experiment" which has more than one "possible outcome," and the problem is to find a number (called "the odds" by some people) which represents the "chance" or "likelihood" that a particular "possible outcome" or set of "possible outcomes" will actually occur. Public-opinion polls, industrial-inspection samples, atomic-particle collision questions, highway traffic surveys, and card games are only a few examples of the many material-world situations which are probability-problem situations. They are often very complicated, but each uses set theory to construct mathematical models for solutions.

For an illustration, here is a probability problem of a sort which might occur in the material world, and which is solved by the use of some very uncomplicated sets. Suppose that Caspar Queeze has had the bad fortune to get himself into a pistol duel, set for early tomorrow morning, with a person who has turned out to be none other than the infamous duelist and marksman, Baron Gunnar von Piercecarcass. Since the agreement is merely to meet "sometime between 5:00 A.M. and 6:00 A.M.," poor Caspar Queeze hopes to satisfy honor and yet also dodge death by arriving between 5:00 A. M. and 5:15 A.M., waiting only three minutes, and then leaving quickly if the Baron has not yet arrived. Now, unknown to Caspar, the Baron is also reluctant about the duel because he has just gotten his trigger finger badly mashed in a coin-return slot. So the poor Baron hopes to satisfy honor and yet also dodge death by arriving between 5:00 A.M. and 5:15 A.M., waiting only two minutes, and then leaving quickly if Caspar Queeze has not yet arrived! If all the times between 5:00 A.M. and 5:15 A.M. are equally likely for the arrival of Caspar on the field of honor, and the same is true for the Baron, what is the probability that the meeting and duel will occur?

Note that if we know the two actual times of arrival, then we also know if the duel occurs. This is a chance situation with infinitely many (indeed uncountably many) possible outcomes, because each possible pair of arrival times for Caspar and the Baron is a possible outcome.

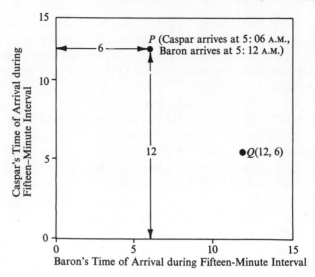

FIGURE 1-2. The Set of All Possible Outcomes
Represented by Points inside a
15 × 15 Square.

The set of all possible outcomes is the sum of two mutually exclusive
sets: the set of all arrival-time pairs which cause a meeting and the set of
all arrival-time pairs which cause no meeting. Let us use points to represent these possible outcomes, and construct our model as follows. Since
each man arrives sometime during a fifteen minute time interval, we consider the set of all points interior to a square which is fifteen units by fifteen
units, as in Figure 1-2. For each point inside the square, let its horizontal
distance from the left side of the square be associated with the time of
arrival of Caspar and let its vertical distance above the bottom base of the
square be associated with the time of arrival of the Baron. Let each
point interior to or on the square be denoted by its pair of distance numbers stated in the order above: Caspar's number stated first and the Baron's
number stated second. For example, point P in Figure 1-2 is denoted by
the ordered number pair (6, 12) because P is 6 units from the left side of
the square and 12 units above the bottom base of the square. The point
P is associated with the possible outcome in which Caspar arrives at six
minutes after the hour of 5:00 A.M. and the Baron arrives at twelve
minutes after the hour. Obviously P is associated with a non-meeting
because, for this case, Caspar would leave at 5:09 A.M., which is before
the Baron arrives. If, on the other hand, it is the Baron who arrives
at 5:06 A.M. and Caspar who arrives at 5:12 A.M., then the ordered pair

(12, 6) and the point Q of Figure 1-2 are used to denote this possible outcome, because we have agreed to always state Caspar's number first and the Baron's number second. Happily, they also miss each other in the case of the possible outcome Q.

We now determine the set of all points which are associated with a meeting-and-duel outcome. (Statisticians would cynically refer to the members of this set as "successes"; let us refer to them as "unfortunate confrontations.") We reason as follows. If Caspar arrives at 5:03, then the Baron must arrive no earlier than 5:01 but no later than 5:06 in order for an unfortunate confrontation to occur. Hence, the point (3, 1) and the point (3, 6) and all points between* (3, 1) and (3, 6) are associated with unfortunate confrontations, as shown in Figure 1-3a. The vertical line-interval PQ in Figure 1-3a is this point set. If, instead, Caspar arrives at 5:10 A.M., then the Baron must arrive no earlier than 5:08 and no later than 5:13 for confrontation to occur. Hence, the points (10, 8) and (10, 13) and all the points between (10, 8) and (10, 13) are associated with confrontation, as is also shown in Figure 1-3a. By extending this reasoning (selecting various times of arrival for Caspar and noting that, for each, the corresponding arrival times for confrontation with the Baron form a vertical line interval as in Figure 1-3a), we see that the set of all possible outcomes

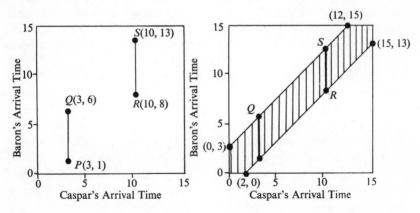

FIGURE 1-3a. All Points of the Vertical Line-Intervals PQ and RS Represent Unfortunate Confrontations.

FIGURE 1-3b. The Shaded Area Is the Set of All Points Associated with Unfortunate Confrontations.

*For a point to be between two other points we shall require all three to be on the same straight line. That is, the three points must not be vertices of some triangle.

which are associated with the meeting-and-duel event are associated with the points of the vertically shaded area in Figure 1-3b. We now suspect that the ratio of the area of the shaded hexagon in Figure 1-3b to the area of the entire square is a number which we should use for the answer to our problem. Hence $68\frac{1}{2}/225$ is the probability of a duel.* At these odds, perhaps the principals should consider oversleeping, but not by the same amount of time.

1-3. SOME PROPERTIES EVERY SET HAS

Although we have agreed to leave *set* and *member* undefined, we can list some properties we want each set to have.

Each Set Must Have a Meaningful Definition

That is, a set M does not exist unless there is some definition D such that each thing either is in M, according to D, or is not in M, according to D, and no thing is both in M and not in M, according to D. For example, "all positive integers" is a meaningful set-definition because each thing either is or is not a positive integer, and there is nothing which is both a positive integer and not a positive integer. On the other hand, "*the* set S of *all* people who like each other" does not make sense. (Note that this does not say, "*a* set of people who *all* like each other!") Suppose Mr. A and Mr. B like each other: then both A and B must be in S because they are people who like each other. Suppose Mr. B and Mr. C like each other: then both B and C must be in S because they are people who like each other. But suppose Mr. A and Mr. C hate each other: then A and C cannot both be in the set S, after all! The trouble arises from the fact that the purported definition of S is actually self-contradictory and is therefore a meaningless collection of words, rather than a definition of a set.

Another example of a non-definition is "the set of all politicians." We cannot decide who are politicians; some of the most influential men on the political scene never run for office but prefer to be "bosses," "king makers" and "powers behind the throne." Surely we would have to call them politicians. But how much political influence must a person have in order to be a politician? We would be unable to agree on a clear meaning for the word "politician." We do not even know what we mean by the word "influence." Hence "the set of all politicians" has no meaning and does not

---

*The number $68\frac{1}{2}$ for the hexagonal area may be obtained from Figure 1-3b, the formula for the area of a triangle, and some scratching of your head.

define a set. In the black-and-white world of mathematics we can avoid such haziness because it is easy to tell if a thing is a mathematical being, such as a point, number, plane or triangle.

The following is an example of one way a definition of a set may be phrased. "Let M denote a set such that a thing is a member of M if and only if that thing is either a point or a circle whose radius is less than ten." Notice that each thing either is or is not a point or a circle whose radius is less than ten, and there is no thing which both is and is not one of these things. Furthermore, there is at least one thing which conforms to the description, so M has at least one member.

In order for a set of words actually to be a definition, it is not necessary that *we* be *able* to decide for each thing whether it satisfies this purported definition. All that is necessary is that each thing either does satisfy or does not satisfy, but does not do both. For example, there exists a set of all china dinner plates which have not been used yet (as of this moment in time), even though it is often impossible for us to remember or determine whether a new plate has yet been used. The important thing is that each china dinner plate either has or has not been used as of this moment in time, irrespective of our knowledge about its history. Therefore, the phrase "all china dinner plates which have never been used" defines a set.

For another example, there exists a set of all people who were born in 1938 and who are alive at this moment. We cannot *determine* for each person whether he is in this set because some people have no birth records and no relatives who know when they were born. Nevertheless, there is such a set because each living person either was or was not born in 1938, regardless of the existence or nonexistence of records of or witnesses to his birth.

Every Set Has at Least One Member

The mind thinks of the notions of *set* and *member* together. Divorcing the notion of *member* from the notion of *set* which we have been discussing would also divorce from *set* all meaning which the human intuition wants. The two notions are, like wire coat hangers, quite inseparable. We cannot imagine a memberless collection or a collection which owes members any more than we can imagine the sound of only one hand clapping, or an artist can imagine a fourth primary color. It is, of course, quite possible to have a meaningful definition without having some thing which qualifies for membership according to the definition. In such a case most people would want to say that there is no such set. To illustrate, we say that there is no Whig Party nowadays, because there are no more Whigs. It is true that the political ideas the Whigs held still exist, but a political party is a set of people and not a set of political ideas. There are no more Whig people; therefore, there is no more Whig Party.

In many textbooks and other literature, when a writer encounters a meaningful definition which is satisfied by nothing, he introduces the term *empty* or the term *null*. Instead of saying, "This set does not exist," which is self-contradictory (how can you talk about it, if it does not exist?), he might say, "This set is empty," or "This is the null set." Unfortunately, this is also self-contradictory because "empty" contradicts the notion of *set* which we want (this is the notion we want for *set* when we use it to solve probability problems). But many writers ignore this latter contradiction in terms and enjoy the convenience of using the words "empty set" instead of the longer phrase "there is nothing which qualifies for membership according to this (meaningful) definition." Let us (you and I) agree to use "there is no such set" where other writers would use "the empty set" or "the null set." Terminology which appeals to the intuition is more satisfying to one who views mathematics as an art form, among other things.

Let us agree then that the statement that there exists a set M means, in part, that there is at least one thing which qualifies for membership in M according to the definition of M. Hence, there does exist a set H such that a thing belongs to H if and only if that thing is the Golden Gate Bridge, because this definition is meaningful and there does exist at least one member: the Golden Gate Bridge. On the other hand, I am sure there is no set K such that a thing is a member of K if and only if that thing is a statue of General Sherman in the city of Atlanta. Even though the definition has meaning, I feel safe in saying that there is no thing which qualifies as a member. Empty-set users would say, "The set K of all statues of General Sherman in the city of Atlanta is the empty set."

For Each Thing There Is a Set
Whose Only Member Is That Thing

For example, there exists a set whose only member is the Golden Gate Bridge. There is a set whose only member is you. If there is to be only one member of a set, then it is easy to state a meaningful definition, and there certainly is at least one member, hence there must be such a set because there are present the first two properties which every set has. *A set is said to be degenerate if and only if it has only one member.*

No Set Is a Member of Itself

Each set must have a meaningful definition, as we have seen, which determines for each thing whether that thing is a member of the set.

In other words, a set is defined in terms of its members. If you allow a set to be one of its own members, then you must state that it is one of the members when you are giving the definition of the set. But you would have to know *already* what the set is in order to refer to it (as a member) in the definition. That is, for a set to be a member of itself, you must already have a definition of the set before you can have a definition of the set! The error committed would be the error of defining a set in terms of itself. We would then encounter such obvious hokum as "Let S denote the set such that a thing is a member of S if and only if that thing is either a point in the plane or the set S which is being defined." The trouble in this example is that S is defined in terms of itself. This kind of error would be committed whenever you allowed a set to be a member of itself. Hence, our notion of *set* requires that *no* set is a member of itself.

There are other lines of argument against allowing a set to be a member of itself. If you regard one set as a member of itself, then, to be consistent, you must require every set to be a member of itself. This leads to absurd situations. Since a basketball team is a five-man set, the team could not be a member of itself because it would have to be one of the men, or the team would have six members. No man is a set. Of course, we sometimes use such loose talk as, "Charlie Flashpast is such a star that he's the whole basketball team!" but we do not really think that Charlie is a five-member set.

In the case of a one-member set, people often confuse the set with the member. Suppose, for example, that the Bill K. Patsy Society for the Advancement of Bill K. Patsy has only one member, a Mr. Bill K. Patsy. This society is a set whose only member is Bill. It is a set, even though it has only one member, because there is a meaningful definition ("the set whose only member is Bill K. Patsy") of it, and there is at least one member. But the society is not the same as its member, because a man is not a set. Indeed, if Bill and the society were one and the same, then the society would be defined as a set whose only member is the set we are defining! The society *must* be different from the man.

For another example, if there were only one member in the Socialist Party, this member would not be the same as the party, because if so then the Socialist Party would be a member of the Socialist Party. If it issued a party card to each member, then the party would be a card-carrying member of itself!

Consider the phrase, "the set of all sets." Does it exist? That is, is there a set M, such that a thing is a member of M if and only if that thing is a set? If so, then, since M itself is a set, M must belong to this "set of all sets;" M would be a member of itself and this contradicts the set notion. Therefore, there is no "set of all sets." There is, of course, such a thing as the set of all points of a space, or the set of all numbers, because these do not involve such a contradiction.

No Thing Is Two Members of a Set

It is ridiculous to say, "There are two smart students in this class, and I am both of them." This is because we never want something to be two members of a set; this would be contradictory to out notions of *set* and *member*. A *sequence*, on the other hand, may have two terms which are the same thing. In the letter sequence *D*, *K*, *W*, *M*, *K*, *A*, *N*, for example, the letter *K* is both the second term and the fifth term. The possibility of repetition is one of the properties which distinguishes the notion of *sequence* from the notion of *set*. We shall discuss sequences later.

Questions

1-1. Suppose the words *is*, *means* and *equals* form a three-word language. Speaking only in this language (i.e., using only these three words), we can define a word in terms of all the others. For example, the sentence "Equals means is," defines *equals* in terms of the other two words in the language. We complete a dictionary of the language with "Is equals means" and "Means is equals." Why hasn't our little dictionary actually defined each word in the language? Does an unabridged English dictionary commit this same logical fallacy?

1-2. Do we mathematicians (you and I) consider three mismatched dining room chairs and an undersized kitchen table as forming a set? Do the first five counting numbers form a set? Do three stamps in some philatelist's stamp collection, ten stamps in my stamp collection, two cancelled stamps in your waste basket, and five stamps for sale in some stamp-dealer's shop form a stamp collection from our point of view? From a stamp collector's point of view?

1-3. Give an example of a number set. Give an example of a set of sets. Give an example of a set of number sets.

1-4. Suppose that "chance situation" (or "experiment") means one toss of a dart at a large circular dart board of radius ten which is close enough so that it will not be missed (not even by Caspar Queeze). Show how you can use some point set in the plane to represent the set of all possible outcomes.

1-5. Copy Figure 1-3b and shade in red the set of all points which are associated with the possible outcomes in which Caspar arrives during the first five minutes and the Baron arrives during the last ten minutes. How much of this red area is associated with unfortunate confrontation (i.e., a duel), and what is the probability of a duel if we know that Caspar does arrive during the first five minutes and the Baron does arrive during the last ten minutes? Now give answers for the case in which we know that Caspar arrives during the first *ten* minutes and the Baron arrives during the last ten minutes.

1-6. Is there a set of all letters of the English alphabet (the present-day alphabet)? Why isn't there a set of all parallel lines? Why isn't there a set of all circles with a common center point? If P is a point in the plane, why is there a set of all circles centered at P? Why isn't there a "set of all nice people" or a "set of all beautiful art objects"?

1-7. Why isn't there a set M such that a thing is a member of M if and only if that thing is either the Easter Bunny or Santa Claus? Is there a set of all kosher hams? Why is there a set K such that a thing is a member of K if and only if that thing is either Santa Claus* or you?

1-8. There has been a sudden and serious decline in the membership of the Grand and Glorious Brotherhood of Toothless Dragons since the Fourth of July parade, when the mascot became excited and gummed a spectator severely. Not only is membership socially unacceptable now because of this atrocity, but there have been more resignations since then which were caused by bickering with Grandpa Tweezle, who was given custody of the cash after the resignation of the treasurer, Orestes McGurk. It seems that Grandpa, drunk with power like a corporal, insisted on paying an unreasonably high price for an asbestos muzzle for the mascot, and all the other remaining members resigned in a huff. Now that Grandpa is the only member, is the Brotherhood the same as Grandpa? Why not?

1-9. Suppose M denotes a set. After you consider the "set of all sets" nonsense mentioned before, tell why there is no "set K such that a thing is a member of K if and only if that thing is not a member of M."

1-10. a. The statement you are now reading is false.
      b. The statement you are now reading is true.
      c. All generalizations are false.

---

*No, Virginia, there is no Santa Claus.

d. Let M denote the set of all things not in M.

e. Let N denote the set whose members are the points of the plane and the set N.

Is one (or more) of the above five sentences a statement? Explain, *before* you read the next part of this question. What is the property common to all five sentences which causes each to be meaningless? (Defining a set in terms of itself is but one example of this property.) Is this property the cause of the dictionary fallacy in Question 1–1?

chapter two

Operations with Sets

2-1. SUBSETS

The statement that B is a subset of A, or that A contains B as a subset, means that B is a set and A is a set and each member of B is a member of A. For instance, the U. S. Senate is a subset of the U. S. Congress because each senator is a congressman. A labor union local is a subset of its labor union because each member of the local is also a member of the labor union. An example involving point sets is Figure 2-1, in which the point set B is a subset of the point set A because each point of B is a point of A. Neither set C nor set D, however, is a subset of A because each has at least one point which is not in A.

It is often important to notice something a statement does *not* say in order to understand it. The subset definition does not say that there is a member of A which is not in B or that the set A is different from the set B. If A and B denote the same set, then B is a subset of A according to the definition of *subset*, because each member of B is a member of A. We see then that, according to the definition of *subset*, each set is a subset of itself.

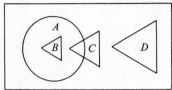

The Point Sets *A*, *B*, *C*, and *D*

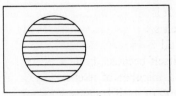

A ∪ *B* (Shaded Area)

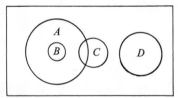

A ∪ *C* (Shaded Area)

A ∪ *D* (Shaded Areas)

FIGURE 2–1. The Unions of Some Point Sets (The point set *A* is the circle plus its interior. Each of the point sets *B*, *C* and *D* is a triangle plus its interior.)

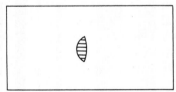

The Point Sets *A*, *B*, *C*, and *D*

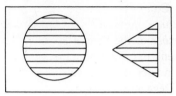

A ∩ *B* (Shaded Area)

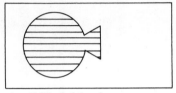

A ∩ *C* (Shaded Area)

There is no point set *A* ∩ *D* because *A* and *D* have no point in common; they are disjoint or mutually exclusive.

FIGURE 2–2. The Intersections of Some Point Sets (Each of the point sets *A*, *B*, *C* and *D* is a circle plus its interior.)

It is important to recognize the distinction between *subset* and *member*. Each set is a subset of itself, but no set is a member of itself. The set K of all points in the plane illustrates this. K is obviously not a *member* of itself because, first, K is not a point—it is a set, and second, no set can be a member of itself, as we saw previously. On the other hand, K is a *subset* of itself because each member of K is a member of K. (I remind you again that the above definition of subset says nothing to imply that the set A is different from the set B.) Another example is the Senate Smogrolling Committee, which is a *subset* of the U. S. Senate because each member of this committee is also a U. S. senator. But the committee is not a *member* of the Senate because the committee is not a senator—it is a *set* of senators. Each senator, on the other hand, is a member of the Senate, but no senator is a subset of the Senate.

Degenerate sets are no exception to this distinction between *subset* and *member*. The set whose only member is the Eiffel Tower is a subset of itself, but not a member of itself. Remember that the *Eiffel Tower* is different from the *set* whose only member is the Eiffel Tower.

The statement that C is a proper subset of A means that C is a subset of A, and there is a member of A which is not a member of C. In the above Senate example, the Smogrolling Committee is a proper subset of the U. S. Senate because there is at least one member, Senator Bill F. Attainder, who is not on this committee. Another illustration is the set $\{1, 2, 3, 4, 5\}$ of the first five counting numbers, which is a proper subset of the set $\{1, 2, 3, 4, 5, 6, 7\}$ of the first seven counting numbers.

Symbols are often used to avoid wordiness in mathematics. In the last example the use of braces, $\{$ and $\}$, to enclose a list of things which form a set is a common way of denoting the set when there are not too many members to list. The symbol $\{a\}$ would denote the set whose only member is a. The symbols $\subseteq$ and $\subset$ respectively mean "is a subset of" and "is a proper subset of," while $\nsubseteq$ and $\not\subset$ mean "is not a subset of" and "is not a proper subset of," respectively. The symbol $\in$ is often used to mean "belongs to." Thus, in the literature $A \subseteq B$ means "A is a subset of B," and $A \subset B$ means "A is a proper subset of B," and $a \in B$ means "a is a member of B."

2-2. UNIONS

If M is a set and N is a set, then each has a meaningful definition. Hence it is meaningful to talk about the set of all members of M or N. *The statement that $M \cup N$ is the union of M with N means that M is a set* *and N is a set and M ∪ N is a set such that a thing is a member of M ∪ N if and only if that thing is a member of M or N.* The union is sometimes called the *sum* in the literature and may be denoted by $M + N$ instead of by $M ∪ N$.

Be sure to understand the meaning of the word "or" in this definition. The words "is a member of *M* or *N*" mean "is a member of *M* only, or of *N* only, *or of both M and N.*" For instance, if you bet that I will go to the movies or to the ball game tomorrow, you will win your bet if I go to the movies only, or to the ball game only, or to *both*. Of course, when someone tells you, "You may take the nickel or the dime," he probably does not want you to take both, but he has been careless enough to speak words which mean that you may take both if you choose. This is true because, if you take both the nickel *and* the dime, then you have taken the nickel; and, if you have taken the nickel, then you have taken the nickel *or* the dime. So when you are asked if you would like pumpkin pie or mince, you are justified in answering "Yes," (although it is the worst kind of folly to be flippant with a person who is cutting pie for you).

If *H* denotes the number set $\{1, 2, 3\}$ and *J* denotes the number set $\{7, 8, 9\}$, then $H ∪ J$ is the set $\{1, 2, 3, 7, 8, 9\}$. In this example, no member is in both *H* and *J*. However the sets *K*, $\{1, 2, 3, 4, 5\}$, and *L*, $\{2, 5, 7, 8\}$, have some members in common. Their union, $K ∪ L$, is the set $\{1, 2, 3, 4, 5, 7, 8\}$. That is, $\{1, 2, 3, 4, 5\} ∪ \{2, 5, 7, 8\} = \{1, 2, 3, 4, 5, 7, 8\}$ if set notation is used. Observe that $K ∪ L$ is not $\{1, 2, 3, 4, 5, 2, 5, 7, 8\}$ because the 2 and 5 would each appear more than once, in contradiction to the fundamental set property that no thing can be two members of the same set.

For another example, suppose *M* is the set $\{1, 2, 3, 4, 5, 6\}$ and *N* is the set $\{2, 4, 6\}$, which is a proper subset of *M*. Then $M ∪ N$ is $\{1, 2, 3, 4, 5, 6\}$.

Figure 2–1 shows some unions of some point sets in the plane. This kind of diagram is referred to as a Venn diagram.

2–3. INTERSECTIONS

If *M* is a set and *N* is a set, then each must have a meaningful definition, and the phrase "all things which are members of both *M* and *N*" has *meaning*, even though *M* may have no members which are also members of *N*. *The statement that M ∩ N is the intersection of M with N or is the common part of M with N means that M is a set and N is a set and M ∩ N is the set such that a thing is a member of M ∩ N if and only if that thing is a member of both M and N.* The symbol $M \cdot N$ is also used to denote the common part of *M* with *N*. Of course, if there is no member common to *M* and *N*, then *M* ∩ *N* does not exist and we cannot talk about it, although those who speak of the "empty set" would rather say that "*M* ∩ *N* is the empty set" to express this nonexistence. *The statement that M and N are mutually exclusive or that M and N are disjoint (or disjunct) means that M and N are sets, and that there is no member of one which is also a member of the other.*

The following are examples of intersecting or disjoint sets. If *K* denotes the number set {1, 2, 3, 4, 5} and *L* denotes the number set {2, 5, 7, 8}, then *K* ∩ *L* is {2, 5}. If *H* denotes the set {1, 2, 3}, then *H* ∩ *L* is {2}, which means the set whose only member is 2. Another example is {1, 2, 3, 4, 5} ∩ {1, 2, 3} = {1, 2, 3}; here one set is a proper subset of the other. On the other hand, there is no member common to both {1, 2, 3} and {7, 8, 9}, so there is no set {1, 2, 3} ∩ {7, 8, 9}; they are mutually exclusive or disjoint number sets. The Venn diagrams in Figure 2–2 give examples of some common parts of some point sets in the plane.

2–4. THE UNIVERSAL SET

Quite often when we are solving a problem which has cropped up in the material world, such as a probability problem, we find it convenient to construct our mathematical model of the situation out of things like sets of points or sets of numbers or sets of number sequences. If so, then there must exist either a set of *all* points in our model, or a set of *all* numbers in our model, or a set of *all* of whatever kind of thing we are using to construct our model. Such a set is referred to as the *universal set* or the *population* for the model, and we shall denote it by *S*, although some writers denote it by *U* or *I*. The entire model is referred to as the *space*.

Are we able to give a careful definition of *S*? We cannot define *S* as "the set of all things," because *S* itself is a thing but *S* cannot be a member of itself. We do not want to define *S* as "the set of all things which are not sets" because this would mean that the Leaning Tower of Pisa would be included in every model. "The set of all members" will not do because a member of a set *A* might itself be another set *B*. I can think of no way we can define *S* (either directly or indirectly) in terms of our other primitive notions of *set*, *member*, and *thing*. Therefore, let us consider *S* as too primitive a notion to define and introduce the *universal set*, *S*, as an undefined term.

In a probability space, *S* is the set of all things which we are using to represent the *possible outcomes*. In the problem of the duel between Caspar and the Baron in Chapter 1, for instance, we constructed our mathematical model out of points and point sets. Each possible outcome was represented by a point which was on or interior to a fifteen by fifteen square, as shown in Figure 1–2. The universal set, S, of all points for this model, then, would be the set of all points on or interior to the fifteen by fifteen square of Figure 1–2. Note that each point set in that model is a subset of S.

An example of a probability problem for which we can conveniently construct a model out of numbers and number sets is the problem of finding the probability that an even number will be scored on one toss of a standard six-sided die (die is the singular of dice). If we assume that there are only six possible outcomes, namely the six possible scores, then we can use the first six counting numbers for our mathematical model of this chance situation. (There are other possible outcomes, such as the die taking an erratic bounce out the window, but we shall ignore these in this chapter.) The set S would be $\{1, 2, 3, 4, 5, 6\}$, a six-member number set. The set of even possible outcomes is represented by the three-member number set $\{2, 4, 6\}$, which is a subset of S. We would want to claim that 3/6 is the probability of an "even" toss.

2–5. COMPLEMENT OF A SET WITH RESPECT TO ANOTHER SET

If A is a set and B is a set then, since there is a meaningful set definition for A and a meaningful set definition for B, the phrase "all members of A which are not in B" has *meaning*, even though there may be no member of A which is not in B. *The statement that $A - B$ is the complement of the set B with respect to the set A, or is the difference between the set A and the set B, means that $A - B$ is the set such that a thing is a member of $A - B$ if and only if that thing is a member of A which is not a member of B.* Of course, if A is a subset of B, then there is no member of A which is not in B and $A - B$ does not exist; the user of the "empty-set" terminology would say that $A - B$ "is the empty set" in this case. If B does not exist, and A *is* a set, then let the symbol $A - B$ mean the set A.

For an illustration of a complement of a set with respect to a set, let A denote the number set $\{2, 3, 4, 5, 6\}$ and let B denote the number set $\{0, 1, 2, 4\}$. Then $A - B$ is $\{3, 5, 6\}$ and $B - A$ is $\{0, 1\}$. If C denotes the set $\{1, 2, 3, 4, 5, 6\}$, then $A - C$ does not exist ("is the empty set") because there is no member of A which is not in C. But $C - A$ is the set $\{1\}$. Figure 2–3 uses point sets to illustrate the idea of differences between sets.

Since S is the universal set for the model, then $S - A$ can be interpreted to mean "not in A," or "not A." Instead of $S - A$, one of the

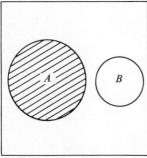

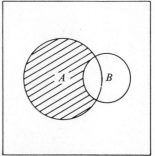

A does not intersect B, and
$A - B$ is shaded set.

A intersects B, and $A - B$ is
shaded point set.
$A - B = A - (A \cap B)$

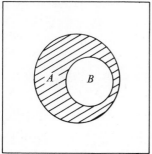

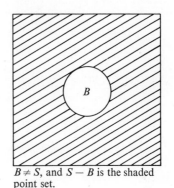

$B \subset A$, and $A - B$ is the shaded
point set.
$A - B = A - (A \cap B)$

$B \neq S$, and $S - B$ is the shaded
point set.

FIGURE 2–3. Venn Diagrams Illustrating Point
Sets $A - B$ and $S - B$ (Notice
that $A - B = A \cap (S - B)$ when
$A \nsubseteq B$.)

symbols A^s, A^c, A^*, $\sim A$, $\bar{A}$, or A' may be used in the literature. We, however, shall use A' later to denote another kind of complementary set.

It is necessary to say a word or two about the order in which operations
are performed when two or more of the union, intersection, and difference
symbols are used in the same expression. The symbol $A \cup B \cap C$ is ambiguous and is avoided. It could mean either $A \cup (B \cap C)$ or $(A \cup B) \cap C$.
The parentheses are grouping symbols which indicate the order in which
we are to proceed. In the case of $A \cup (B \cap C)$ we are to intersect B with
C first to obtain $B \cap C$ and then unite $B \cap C$ with A. But for
$(A \cup B) \cap C$, we are to obtain $A \cup B$ first and then consider its intersection with C. For the same reasons, $A - B - C$ and $A - B \cup C$ and
$A - B \cap C$ and $A \cup B - C$ and $A \cap B - C$ are each ambiguous and

require parentheses. Since $A \cup B \cup C$ and $(A \cup B) \cup C$ and $A \cup (B \cup C)$ are all the same, we can omit parentheses in this case. We can also omit parentheses from $A \cap B \cap C$, because $(A \cap B) \cap C$ $= A \cap (B \cap C)$.

As we noted before, there are no sets $A - A$ and $A - S$. Each "is the empty set." If $B \cap A$ exists, let us define $A - (A - B)$ to be $A \cap B$.

What about the case of the symbol $[(D - A) \cap A] \cup C$? Notice that $D - A$ and A have no common part, and therefore there is no set $(D - A) \cap A$. Hence our *union* definition in Section 2–2 does not apply, because it only mentions, "the *statement* that $M \cup N$ is the union of M with N," and gives no clue about a case in which M does not exist, thus preventing the phrase, "$M \cup N$ is the union of M with N," from being a statement. Let us now fill in this gap. *If M does not exist* (i.e., there is a meaningful definition for M, but nothing qualifies to be a member of M according to this definition) *and N is a set, then let the symbols $M \cup N$ and $N \cup M$ each mean N.* Then $[(D - A) \cap A] \cup C$ means the set C, according to this definition. Also, $(S - S) \cup A = A$ and $(B - S) \cup A$ $= A$, if A exists.

2–6. SIMILARITY OF SET OPERATIONS TO THE COMPOUNDING OF STATEMENTS

Suppose we are considering two or more statements which concern the same topic or subject. The truth or falsity of each of our statements is perhaps* determined by what is true about the subject. But suppose we are ignorant of some or all of the facts about the subject, so that, from our point of view, we should speculate about the truth of our statements in the light of *each* of the sets of facts which is *possible* for the subject. Let each such possible set of facts about the subject be herein referred to as a *condition* of the subject, for want of a better word. As a result of our uncertainty about the true condition of the subject, for *each* of the statements we are considering there are conditions of the subject which make that statement true and conditions of the subject which make that statement false.

Consider, for instance, the following two statements.

Statement g: Ed has gallstones.
Statement m: Ed is allergic to emu feathers.

The topic, of course, is Ed's medical condition, which could be anything

---

*I say "perhaps" because there are statements which are true regardless of the condition of the subject. For example, the statement, "If Joe is bald, then Joe is bald," is true whether Joe is bald or bushy.

from a state of complete health to a state of physical collapse accompanied by glanders and a slow chill around the liver. For *each* health condition which is possible for Ed, Statement *g* is either true or false and Statement *m* is either true or false.

Let the set of all possible conditions of a subject be represented by the set of all points in a Venn diagram. Then for each statement *b* about the subject, the set of all possible conditions for which *b* is true (assuming *b* *can* be true) is represented by some point set *B* on the Venn diagram. Then each point not in *B* (i.e., each point in $S - B$) represents a condition of the subject for which statement *b* is false. You might say that a "picture" of a statement is the set of all points on a Venn diagram for which the statement is true. Some writers refer to this point set as the *truth set* for the statement.

To illustrate, let the set of all possible medical conditions for Ed be denoted by the set *S* of all points in the Venn diagrams of Figure 2–4. Let *G* denote the set of all points representing conditions in which State-

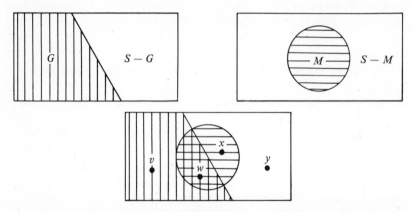

The rectangular point set represents the set of all possible "conditions of the topic." Each point in the point set *G* represents a medical condition in which Statement *g* (Ed has gallstones) is true. Therefore, each point in point set *S-G* represents a medical condition in which Statement *g* is false (Ed has no gallstones). Each point in point set *M* represents a medical condition in which Statement *m* is true. Hence, each point in point set *S-M* represents a medical condition of Ed in which statement *m* is false (Ed is not allergic to emu feathers). Point *v*, which is in point sets *G* and *S-M*, is an example of a condition in which Statement *g* is true and Statement *m* is false (i.e., a medical condition in which Ed has gallstones but is not allergic to emu feathers). Then $G \cap (S - M)$ denotes the set of points for which *g* is true *and* *m* is false; $G \cup M$ denotes set of all points for which *g* is true *or* *m* is true. The point set $M \cap (S - G)$ denotes set of all points for which, "If Ed is allergic to emu feathers, then Ed has gallstones," is a false statement. Hence, for all other points (i.e., for the point set $G \cup (S - M)$) the statement, "If *m*, then *g*," is true.

FIGURE 2–4.

ment g, about Ed's gallstones, is true. Then $S - G$ would depict the set of all medical conditions in which Statement g is false and Ed does not have gallstones. Likewise, let M denote the set of all points for medical conditions in which Statement m is true. Observe that only for conditions represented by the points in $G \cap M$ are Statements g and m both true. Hence $G \cap M$ denotes the set of all conditions in which the statement, "Ed has gallstones *and* Ed is allergic to emu feathers," is a true statement. That is, the points in G *and* M represent the conditions in which the Statements g *and* m are true, and we see that the set relationship $\cap$ is analogous to the *and* relationship between statements. In a similar manner we find that $G \cup M$ denotes the set of all conditions which make the statement, "g is true *or* m is true," a true statement. We conclude, then, that the union relationship between sets parallels the *or* relationship between statements.

Now consider the question of which point set in Figure 2–4 represents the set of all conditions in which the more complex statement, "*If* Ed is allergic to emu feathers, *then* Ed has gallstones," is a true statement. To answer this, we observe that the *only* ways this complex statement can be *false* are the conditions in which Ed *is* allergic to emu feathers but does *not* have gallstones (i.e., the conditions in which m is true and g is false), and these conditions are denoted by the points which are in M but not in G: the point set $M \cap (S - G)$. Then for all other points [i.e., the point set $(S - M) \cup G$] the statement, "If Ed is allergic to emu feathers, then he has gallstones," is a true statement, and Ed had better steer clear of those emus.

It should be emphasized that only those statements which are appropriate to the topic of discussion should be represented as point sets in the Venn diagram for that topic. For instance, in the preceding example there is no point set which represents the statement "A moose is a hatrack with a mind of its own," because this statement is meaningless within the narrow context of Ed's medical condition. We would require a different topic and a different space S in order to represent this last statement as a point set on a Venn diagram. Naturally, if we want to use only one Venn diagram to portray two or more statements, we must choose a topic or subject for S which is broad enough to encompass *all* the statements.

The union, intersection, and difference relationships between sets, which are often represented by the symbols, $\cup$, $\cap$ and $-$, respectively, are referred to as *operations on sets* by some people. Each operation parallels some "connective," or fundamental kind of relationship between simple statements. This fact was strongly suggested by the foregoing medical example. That is, $A \cap B$ parallels the "and" relationship: Statement a is true *and* Statement b is true. But $A \cup B$ parallels the "or" relationship between statements: Statement *a* is true *or* Statement *b* is true. $S - A$ is like the "not "modifier: *not* Statement *a*, which means Statement *a* is *not* true. The $A - B$ relationship is like the "unless" relationship: Statement *a* is true *unless* Statement *b* is true. Furthermore, $(S - A) \cup B$ parallels the "if, then" relationship: *if* Statement *a* is true, *then* Statement *b* is true. Finally, $[(S - A) \cup B] \cap [(S - B) \cup A]$ is analogous to the "if and only if" relationship: Statement *a* is true *if and only if* Statement *b* is true.* These ideas are illustrated in Figure 2–5 on the next page.

Observe that if you sketch a diagram in which $A \subseteq B$, then, "If *a*, then *b*," is true for *all* points of *S*. For example, the statement, "If Ed is dead, then Ed is not feeling well," is true for all Ed's possible medical conditions and the statement is represented by the set *S*, as can be seen in Sketch 9 of Figure 2–5. Observe, also, that when our Venn diagram shows that $A = B$, then the statement, "*a* is true if and only if *b* is true," is true for all conditions, and the statement is represented by *S*. Figure 2–5 also illustrates this.

Venn–diagram representation is useful when we encounter two complicated statements, each of which is composed of simpler statements which are related by one or more of the *or*, *and*, *is not*, *unless*, *if then*, and *if and only if* relationships. We can tell whether our two complicated statements contradict each other, are equivalent to each other, or are neither contradictory nor equivalent, by the use of a Venn diagram. The technique can be shown by example. Consider the following statements.

> Statement   I: We need Elmo *and not* Dave *if and only if* we need Fred.
> Statement   II: *If* we need Dave, *then* we either need Elmo *or* do *not* need Fred.
> Statement III: We need Elmo *or* Dave *if and only if* we do *not* need Fred.

Are Statements I and II compatible? Are Statements I and III compatible? To answer these questions we first notice that each of these three more complicated statements is a relationship between the three simpler statements "We need Dave," and "We need Elmo," and "We need Fred." Let us denote these three simpler statements by *d*, *e* and *f* respectively. On some Venn diagram whose points represent all possible conditions of some subject broad enough to encompass all three statements, we shall let point sets *D*, *E*, and *F* represent the sets of all conditions for which Statement *d* is true, Statement *e* is true, and Statement *f* is true, respectively.

---

*Cangelosi, *Compound Statements and Mathematical Logic*, should be consulted for an explanation of connectives, simple and compound statements, their truth values, and logical relationships.

A is shaded set.

Points of A for which Statement a Is True

B is shaded set.

Points of B for which Statement b Is True

A ∩ B is shaded.

Points of A ∩ B for which the Statement, "a Is True and b Is True," Is True

A ∪ B is shaded.

Points of A ∪ B for which the Statement, "a Is True or b Is True," Is True

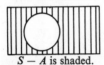

S − A is shaded.

Points of S − A for which the Statement, "a Is not True," Is True

A − B is shaded.

Points of A − B for which the Statement, "a Is True unless b Is True," Is True

(S − A) ∪ B is shaded.

Points of (S − A) ∪ B for which the Statement, "If a Is True, then b Is True," Is True

[(S − A) ∪ B] ∩ [(S − B) ∪ A] is shaded.

Points of [(S − A) ∪ B] ∩ [(S − B) ∪ A] for which the Statement, "a Is True if and only if b Is True," Is True

A is interior of square; B is interior of circle.

S Is Set of Points for which, "If a, then b," Is True when A ⊆ B.

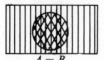

A = B

S Is Set of All Points for which, "a Is True if and only if b Is True," Is True when A = B.

FIGURE 2–5. Analogies between Statement Relationships and Set Operations

26

Now in Statement I we replace d, e, f, *and*, *or*, and *not* by the symbols D, E, F, $\cap$, $\cup$ and S —, respectively, to get the partial translation, "$E \cap (S - D)$ if and only if F." Then, using the analogy between "a if and only if b" and $[(S - A) \cup B] \cap [(S - B) \cup A]$ to replace the words

 $E \cap (S - D)$, which is $E \cap \tilde{D}$

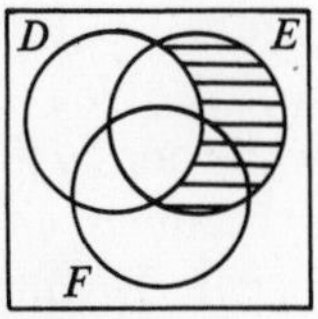

 $\{S - [E \cap (S - D)]\} \cup F$, which is $\widetilde{E \cap \tilde{D}} \cup F$

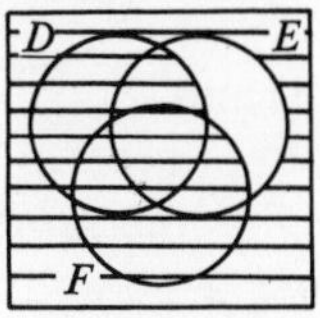

 $[S - F] \cup [E \cap (S - D)]$, which is $\tilde{F} \cup (E \cap \tilde{D})$

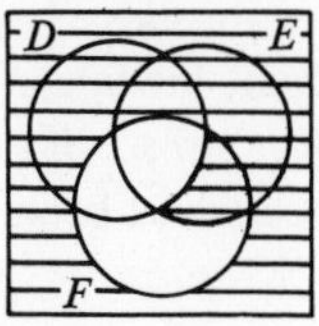

FIGURE 2–6a. Three Steps to Aid in Constructing Venn Diagram for Statement I

 $\{\{S - [E \cap (S - D)]\} \cup F\} \cap \{[S - F] \cup [E \cap (S - D)]\}$, which is $[\widetilde{E \cap \tilde{D}} \cup F] \cap [\tilde{F} \cup (E \cap \tilde{D})]$, is the shaded area.

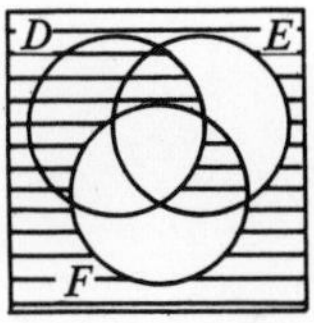

FIGURE 2–6b. Venn Diagram Which Represents Statement I (Points in shaded areas represent conditions of the subject for which Statement I is true. Notation can be simplified by replacing $S - X$ with $\tilde{X}$, so that $(S - X) \cup Y$ becomes $\tilde{X} \cup Y$.)

"if and only if," Statement I becomes $\{\{S - [E \cap (S - D)]\} \cup F\} \cap \{[S - F] \cup [E \cap (S - D)]\}$. This point set is illustrated in Figures 2–6a and 2–6b.

Yes, I can hear you complaining that this notation has become complicated to the point where this last expression is crawling across half the page. Let us simplify it, before it starts to feed on Figure 2–6. For each set X, let us replace the symbol $S - X$ with the symbol $\tilde{X}$. Now our "If a, then b" analogy, $[(S - A) \cup B]$, becomes $\tilde{A} \cup B$, while our "a if and only if b" analogy, $[(S - A) \cup B] \cap [(S - B) \cup A]$, becomes $(\tilde{A} \cup B) \cap (\tilde{B} \cup A)$. The caterpillar obtained from Statement I simplifies to $[\tilde{E} \cap \tilde{D} \cup F] \cap [\tilde{F} \cup (E \cap \tilde{D})]$, which seems less voracious now. This point set is the shaded point set in Figure 2–6b.

Statements II and III translate into $\tilde{D} \cup (E \cup \tilde{F})$ and $[\widetilde{E \cup D} \cup \tilde{F}] \cap [\tilde{F} \cup E \cup D]$, respectively. (The $\tilde{A} \cup B$ relationship is used to translate the "*if, then*" part of Statement II.) Observe that $\tilde{\tilde{F}}$ is the same as F.

By comparing the two Venn diagrams in Figures 2–6b and 2–7a, we find that, at each point for which I is true, II is also true. Hence, if Statement I is true, then Statement II is true. That is, I implies II. But there are points for which Statement II is true and Statement I is false. This is so because the shaded point set in Figure 2–6b is a *proper* subset of the shaded point set in Figure 2–7a. If these two shaded point sets had been the same

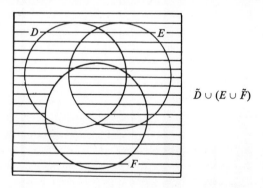

$$\tilde{D} \cup (E \cup \tilde{F})$$

FIGURE 2–7a. Venn Diagram for Statement II (Notice that the shaded set in Figure 2–6b is proper subset of shaded set in Figure 2–7a. Therefore, if Statement I is true, then Statement II is true, but there are points for which Statement II is true and Statement I is false.)

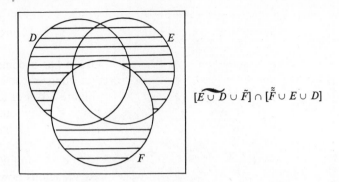

$$[\widehat{E \cup D} \cup \tilde{F}] \cap [\widetilde{\tilde{F} \cup E} \cup D]$$

FIGURE 2–7b. Venn Diagram for Statement III

point set, it would have meant that Statements I and II were *equivalent* (i.e., the truth of one would imply the truth of the other). If, on the other hand, the shaded point sets in one diagram had been the same as the unshaded point sets in the other, then the two Statements I and II would have been *inconsistent* (i.e., mutually contradictory).

By comparing Figures 2–6b and 2–7b, we see points for which Statements I and III are both true, points for which both are false, points for which I is true and III is false and points for which III is true and I is false. Hence, I and III are neither equivalent nor inconsistent, and neither statement implies the other.

2-7. SOME PROBLEM-SOLVING WITH VENN DIAGRAMS

Suppose we have a black bag containing exactly thirty items, of which exactly fourteen are green, exactly thirteen are made of rubber, exactly nine are cubical,* exactly five are both green and rubber, exactly seven are both green and cubical, exactly four are both rubber and cubical, and exactly three are green, rubber and cubical. How many of the objects are neither green nor rubber nor cubical?

To answer this we may draw a Venn diagram showing three point sets which intersect as shown in Figure 2–8. We will use these three sets to represent the set of green objects, the set of rubber objects, and the set of cubical objects, respectively, so let us denote the three sets by G, R, and C. Now we try to account for as many of the thirty objects as possible by

---

*Notice that fourteen, thirteen, and nine add up to more than thirty, which is the total number of objects. The discrepancy is caused by common parts.

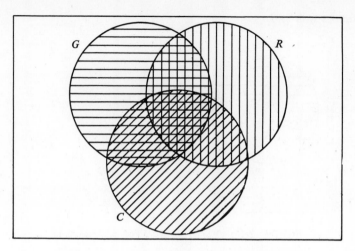

FIGURE 2–8a. Venn Diagram for the Green-
Rubber-Cubical-Objects Prob-
lem (The green set, G, is
horizontally lined, the rubber
set, R, is vertically lined, and
the cubical set, C, is diagonally
lined. S is the interior of the
rectangle.)

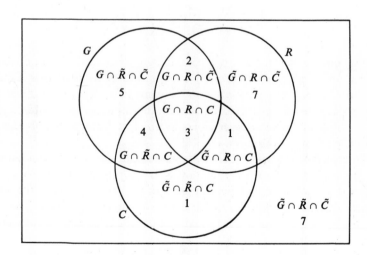

FIGURE 2–8b. Solution to the G-R-C Problem

labelling each of the sets $G \cap R \cap C$, $G \cap R \cap \tilde{C}$, $G \cap \tilde{R} \cap C$, $\tilde{G} \cap R \cap C$, $G \cap \tilde{R} \cap \tilde{C}$, $\tilde{G} \cap R \cap \tilde{C}$, $\tilde{G} \cap \tilde{R} \cap C$ and $\tilde{G} \cap \tilde{R} \cap \tilde{C}$ with the number of members it contains. Since there are three green rubber cubical objects, we label $G \cap R \cap C$ with a three. Since there are only five objects which are both green and rubber and three of them are already accounted for in the set $G \cap R \cap C$, there must be only two objects which are both green and rubber but not cubical; we place a two in the set $G \cap R \cap \tilde{C}$ on the Venn diagram. In this manner we determine the number of members of each set on the Venn diagram and find that in order for the grand total to be thirty, there must be seven objects which are neither green nor rubber nor cubical.

For a problem which is slightly more complicated, suppose that Professor Chalkstorm Q. van Whitesleeves, the abominable snowman of set theory, takes a poll of his class during their final exam and finds that some students think that set theory is the greatest thing since sarsaparilla, some think that it will probably replace night baseball, and some think that it is the answer to color television. Let A, B, and C, respectively, denote these three subsets of the class. The two students who were not in subsets A or B or C say that, "A set is a set. When you've seen one, you've seen them all. What's the big fuss about?" Denote this subset by F. If (1) exactly 18 students in subset C are not in A or B, and (2) only 23 in C are not in B, and (3) only 25 in A are not in B, and (4) only 48 students are in A or B, and (5) only 48 students are in A or C, and (6) there are five times as many students who are in both A and B as there are students who are in A and B and C; how many students are in the class, and how many were wise enough to be in all three subsets A, B, and C?

To answer this, we restate the above information in set notation.

(1) No. of $C \cap A^s \cap B^s = 18$.   (2) No. of $C \cap B^s = 23$.
(3) No. of $A \cap B^s = 25$.   (4) No. of $A \cup B = 48$.
(5) No. of $A \cup C = 48$.   (6) No. of $A \cap B =$
$\qquad\qquad\qquad\qquad\qquad\qquad\qquad 5 \times$ no. of $A \cap B \cap C$.
(7) No. of $F = 2$ and $F = A^s \cap B^s \cap C^s$.

The Venn diagram, shown in Figure 2–9, is filled in as follows. From fact (1) we place an 18 in $C \cap A^s \cap B^s$. From facts (1) and (2) we see that $A \cap C \cap B^s$ has only 5 members. This result plus fact (3) shows us that $A \cap B^s \cap C^s$ has exactly 20 members. Facts (1) and (4) mean that $A \cup B \cup C$ has exactly $18 + 48$, or 66 members. This last result plus fact (5) yield the information that the number of members of $B \cap A^s \cap C^s$ is $66 - 48$, or 18. We now have 61 of the 66 members in $A \cup B \cup C$ accounted for on the Venn diagram, Figure 2–9b. There are only 5 members remaining to be distributed to the sets $A \cap B \cap C^s$ and $A \cap B \cap C$ and $B \cap C \cap A^s$. This plus fact (6) implies that $A \cap B$ contains all 5

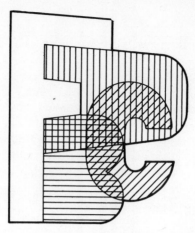

FIGURE 2-9a. Venn Diagram for the Professor
Chalkstorm Q. van Whitesleeves
Example. (The question of which
areas represent the sets A, B,
C, and F is a smasher which is
left as an exercise for the
reader. Of course, S is A ∪ B
∪ C ∪ F and is outlined by a
heavy black border.)

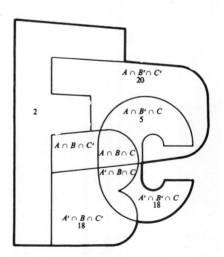

FIGURE 2-9b. Same Venn Diagram with Numbers Gleaned from Facts (1)
through (7).

and $A \cap B \cap C$ contains exactly one member and there are none left for $B \cap C \cap A^s$ (which therefore does not exist). Of course, $A \cap B \cap C^s$ contains exactly 4 students. Fact (7) now shows us that the whole class contains exactly $66 + 2$ students.

2–8. PARTITIONS

In Figure 2–9b the set $A \cup B \cup C$ was broken down into seven mutually-exclusive subsets in order to solve a problem. This "breaking down" of a set into mutually-exclusive subsets is sometimes referred to as *partitioning* a set, and the collection of subsets is called a *partition*. A partition is a *collection*: it is a collection of *sets*. In Figure 2–9b the partition has only *seven* members, each of which is itself a set having *infinitely* many members—all points. *The statement that A is a partition of the set X means that A is a collection of mutually-exclusive subsets of X, such that the union of them all is X.* (Some people also call $\{X\}$ a partition of X.) *Subdivision* is another word for *partition*. Each member of a partition is said to be a *cell* of that partition. If the state of New Jersey, for example, can be regarded as a point set, then the *set* of all its twenty-one counties is a *partition* of the point set New Jersey, because the counties are mutually exclusive point sets and their union is the point set New Jersey. Each county is a cell. Notice the distinction between the members of the set New Jersey and the members of the partition. The members of New Jersey are *points*, and there are infinitely many of them; but the members of the partition are *counties*, and there are only twenty-one of them. Hence, no member of New Jersey is a member of the partition. You may have overlooked this fact; it is an error many people make the first time they are presented with a set of sets.

The union of the members of a partition is, of course, the set which is partitioned. *The statement that the sets B_1, B_2, B_3, ..., B_n fill up the set A or exhaust the set A means that $B_1 \cup B_2 \cup B_3 \cup ... \cup B_n = A$.* On the other hand, *the statement that the collection D of sets: $\{D_1, D_2, D_3, ..., D_n\}$ covers the set A means that each member of A is a member of some set in the collection D.* These terms are illustrated in Figure 2–10.

If A is a set and B is a *subdivision* of A and some or all of the members of B are themselves partitioned, the result is called a *refinement* of B. *If B is a partition of the set A, then the statement that C is a refinement of B means that C is a partition of A which has the property that each member of C is a subset of some member of B.* Observe that, according to this definition, each subdivision is a refinement of itself. To illustrate the refinement idea with the New Jersey counties example, let us assume that every point

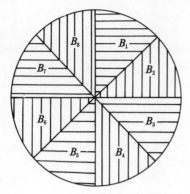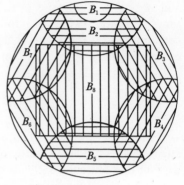

(a) In each case the sets $\{B_1, B_2, \cdots, B_8\}$ *fill up*, or *exhaust*, the set A, which is the interior of the large circle. *Only* the *left* diagram shows $\{B_1, B_2, B_3, \cdots, B_8\}$ *partitioning* the interior of the circle.

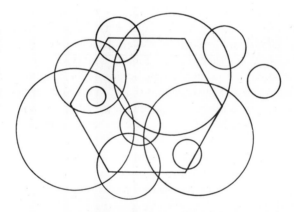

(b) The members of D, the set of all the circle-interiors, cover the set A, the hexagon-interior.

FIGURE 2–10. Examples of a Collection of Sets *Filling* Up a Set A and a Collection of Sets *Covering* a Set A

of New Jersey is in some municipal district (cities, towns, and townships) and that no municipal district crosses a county line. This is a risky assumption, but let us assume it, anyway. Then the *set* of all New Jersey municipal districts is a refinement of the twenty-one-county subdivision of the state. For another illustration, when a family's farmland is divided among the sons, this is a partition of the farmland. Then, when some or all of the sons divide their land among their sons, the resulting set of all plots is a refinement of the partition.

Another example of a refinement is the Topheavy Corporation, whose personnel can be partitioned into four subsets: manufacturing personnel (10 per cent), sales personnel (10 per cent), office personnel (30 per cent) and management (50 per cent). This partition can be *refined* as follows. Of the manufacturing personnel, 40 per cent are loyal men, 30 per cent are loyal women, and 30 per cent are industrial spies who are seeking the corporation's top-secret process for the manufacture of wash-and-wear spats. Of the sales staff, 50 per cent are loyal men and 50 per cent are spies. Of the office staff, 20 per cent are loyal men, 50 per cent are loyal women, and 30 per cent are spies. Of the management, 20 per cent are loyal men, 10 per cent are loyal women, and 70 per cent are spies. Thus, the partition is further broken down into eleven subsets of 4 per cent, 3 per cent, 3 per cent, 5 per cent, 5 per cent, 6 per cent, 15 per cent, 9 per cent, 10 per cent, 5 per cent and 35 per cent, and this list is an eleven-member refinement of the four-member partition. Figure 2–11a is called a *tree diagram* and is one way of portraying this refinement of a partition. In Figure 2–11b are point-set representations of the partition and the refinement.

A stained-glass window is a crude example of a partition. If two stained-glass windows of different patterns are held against each other, the resulting pattern is not only a refinement of both, it is a special kind of refinement of both which is referred to as a *cross-partition. If B_1 and B_2 are each partitions of the set A, then the statement that C is the cross-partition of B_1 and B_2 means that C is the partition of A which has the property that each member of C is the common part of some member of B_1 with some member of B_2.* Figures 2–12a and 2–12b illustrate various cross-partitions of three partitions of a point set A, which is the interior of a circle. Notice that each cell of the cross-partition of partitions B and C is the common part of two cells, one in B and one in C. Also observe in Figure 2–12b that B and D are partitions which are arranged so that the number of cells in their cross-partition is the maximum possible for the cross–partition of an eight–member partition and a six-member partition—namely 8×6, or 48. It is easy to see that there are at most $m \times n$ cells in the cross-partition of an m-member partition and an n-member partition.

In the example of the Topheavy Corporation, the personnel are 25 per cent loyal men, 23 per cent loyal women and 52 per cent spies, as can be seen from Figure 2–11b. This partition and the manufacturing-sales–office-management partition have a cross-partition which is the eleven-member refinement. Figure 2–11b, however, is inappropriate for the cross-partition because of the geometric arrangement of the sets.

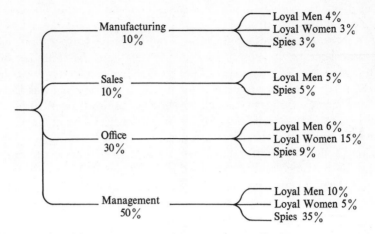

FIGURE 2–11a. Tree Diagram for the Topheavy
Corporation

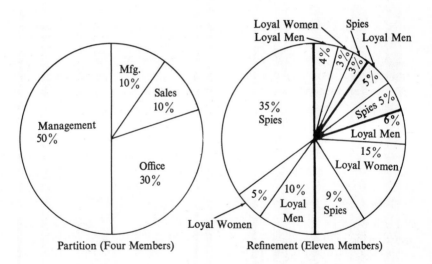

FIGURE 2–11b. A Point-Set Representation of
the   Topheavy   Corporation
Partition and Refinement

    The set of income and expense accounts of the Acme Wholesale Corporation, just before net income is computed, is partitioned into accounts with credit balances and accounts with debit balances as in the list below. Credit balances are in parentheses. The set is also partitioned into net-sales accounts, cost-of-goods-sold accounts, operating-expense accounts

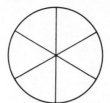

Eight-Member
Partition *B*

Six-Member
Partition *C*

Six-Member
Partition *D*

FIGURE 2–12a. Three Partitions of the Interior
of a Circle

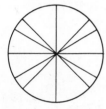

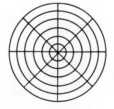

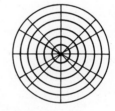

The Twelve-Member
Cross-partition of *B*
and *C*

Forty–eight-Member
Cross-partition of *B*
and *D*

The Seventy–two-Member
Cross-partition of *B*, *C*
and *D*.

FIGURE 2–12b. Two Cross-partitions (Observe
that the maximum number of
cells which can be in the cross-
partition of an eight-member
partition and a six-member
partition is 6 × 8, or 48.)

and other-income-and-expense accounts. The cross–partition of these two
partitions is the seven-member set of all the dollar balances in the list of
entries below and at the top of p. 38.

	Debits	Credits
Net Sales:		
Gross Sales	$	$(100,000)
Sales Returns	500	
Cost of Goods Sold:		
Purchases and Initial	70,000	
Inventory		
Ending Inventory		(20,000)

	Debits	*Credits*
Operating Expenses:		
Selling, Administrative,		
and Other Expenses	30,000	
Other Income and Expense:		
Interest Income		(200)
Loss on Sale of Building	1,000	

Of course, from the accountant's point of view, this classification is too coarse to be useful, and he will use a refinement of this set of dollar amounts (as well as a more informative format) for his profit and loss statement.

We shall see more of partitions later.

Questions

2-1. Why can not a set be a proper subset of itself? List all fifteen subsets of the set $\{1, 2, 3, 4\}$. (The empty-set user, unintimidated by the nonexistence of the "empty set," would list sixteen subsets.) Why can't you *list* all the subsets of the X axis? What symbol would denote the set of all points inside the rectangle, but not inside or on the circle, in Figure 2-1?

2-2. Suppose A is a set, B is a set, and C is a set. Explain why each statement in group a. is false and why each statement in group b. is true.*
  a. 1. If $A \subseteq B$, then $B \subset A$.
   2. If $A \subset B$, then $B \subseteq A$.
   3. If $A \subseteq B$, then $B \subseteq A$.
  b. 1. If $A \subset B$ and $B \subset C$, then $A \subset C$.
   2. If $A \subseteq B$ and $B \subseteq C$, then $A \subseteq C$.
   3. If $A \subset S$, then there is a set $\tilde{A}$.
   4. No set A has two complements with respect to another set B.
   5. There is no set $A \cap (B - A)$.

2-3. Why is the statement, "If A is a set and B is a set, then $A \cap B$ is a set," a false statement? From the properties that every set has, in Chapter 1, explain why it is true that, if x exists, then there exists a set $\{x\}$.

---

*A statement is true only if it is true in every case for which that statement has meaning. One way to show that a statement is false is to present at least one counterexample (exception) to it. Now do not tell me that "the exception proves the rule." If the exception proves the rule, then the example of Adolf Hitler would prove that every man is a humanitarian.

2–4. From the definitions of union, intersection, and complement, we can see that the symbols $A \cup B$ and $A \cap B$ and $\tilde{A}$ can be interpreted in English as "in A or B" and "in A and B" and "not in A," respectively. Interpret $A \cap \tilde{B}$, $\tilde{A} \cup B$, $\tilde{A} \cap \tilde{B}$, $\tilde{A} \cup \tilde{B}$, $(B - A) \cup (A - B)$, $(A - B) \cap \tilde{A}$, $A \cup (B \cap C)$, $(A \cup B) \cap C$, $(A \cup B) \cap (A \cup C)$, $(\tilde{B} \cap A) \cup (\tilde{A} \cap B)$, $A - (C - B)$ and $(A - C) - B$.

2–5. Assume the point sets P and Q intersect and that neither is a subset of the other. For each of the following point sets sketch a Venn diagram and shade the area which represents it.

$$P \cap Q \qquad \tilde{P} \cup \tilde{Q} \qquad (Q - P) - (P - Q)$$
$$P \cap \tilde{Q} \qquad \tilde{P} - Q \qquad \tilde{Q} \cap (P \cup Q)$$
$$\tilde{P} \cup Q \qquad P - \tilde{Q} \qquad (Q - P) \cup [(P - Q) \cap \tilde{Q}]$$
$$\tilde{P} \cap \tilde{Q} \qquad \tilde{P} - \tilde{Q}$$

2–6. Explain why each of the following is true.
  a. $A \subseteq A \cup B$.
  b. If $A \subseteq B$ and $B \subseteq A$, then $A = B$.
  c. If $A \cap B$ exists, then $A \cap B \subseteq A$.
  d. If $A \cup B \subseteq A$, then $B \subseteq A$.
  e. If $B \subseteq A \cap B$, then $B \subseteq A$.
  f. If $A \cap B = A$, then $A \subseteq B$.
  g. If $A \cup B = B$, then $A \subseteq B$.
  h. If $A \cup B = A$ and $A \cap B = B$, then $B \subseteq A$.
  i. $A \cap B \subseteq A \cup B$, if $A \cap B$ exists.
  j. If $A \subseteq B$, then $A \cap B = A$ and $A \cup B = B$.
  k. $A \cup B = B \cup A$. } Commutative
  l. $A \cap B = B \cap A$. } Properties
  m. $A \cup (B \cup C) = (A \cup B) \cup C$. } Associative
  n. $A \cap (B \cap C) = (A \cap B) \cap C$. } Properties
  o. If $A \cup B = A \cup C$ and $A \cap B = A \cap C$, then $B = C$.
  p. $A \cup \tilde{A} = S$.
  q. $A \cup (B - A) = A \cup B$.
  r. If $A \subset B$, then $(B - A) \cup A = B$.
  s. If $\tilde{A} = \tilde{B}$, then $A = B$.
  t. If $A = B$, then $\tilde{A} = \tilde{B}$.
  u. There is only one set, namely S, which contains every set as a subset.
  v. $A - B = A \cap \tilde{B}$, if $B \subset A$.
  w. $A - B = A - (A \cap B)$, if $A \not\subseteq B$.
  x. $\tilde{A} \cap \tilde{B} = A \widetilde{\cup} B$. } de Morgan's Laws
  y. $\tilde{A} \cup \tilde{B} = A \widetilde{\cap} B$. }

2–7. For each statement below, you may sketch Venn diagrams to understand why it is true; then use the English *language only* (no diagrams) to explain why it is true. Assume in each case that A, B, C and S are different sets and $A \cap B \cap C$ exists.

a. $A \cap (B \cup C) = (A \cap B) \cup (A \cap C)$. ⎫ Distributive
b. $A \cup (B \cap C) = (A \cup B) \cap (A \cup C)$. ⎭ Properties
c. $\widetilde{\tilde{A} \cap \tilde{B}} = A \cup B$.
d. $\widetilde{\tilde{A} \cup \tilde{B}} = A \cap B$.
e. $A \cap \tilde{B} = A - (A \cap B)$.
f. $B = (B \cap A) \cup (B \cap \tilde{A})$.
g. $A \cup B = B \cup (A \cap \tilde{B}) = A \cup (B \cap \tilde{A})$.
h. $(A - B) \cup \tilde{A} = \tilde{B}$.
i. $(A - B) \cup B = A \cup B$.
j. If B intersects A, then $A - (A - B) = B \cap A$.
k. $\tilde{\tilde{B}} = B$.
l. $A \widetilde{-} B = \tilde{A} \cup B$.
m. $(A - B) - C = A - (B \cup C)$.
n. $A - (B - C) = (A - B) \cup (A \cap C) =$
   $(A - B) \cup (A \cap C \cap B)$.
o. $A \cup (B - C) = (A \cup B) - (C - A) = A \cup (B \cap \tilde{C})$.
p. $(A \cup B) - C = (A - C) \cup (B - C) = (A \cup B) \cap \tilde{C}$.
q. $A \cap (B - C) = (A \cap B) - (A \cap C) = A \cap B \cap \tilde{C}$.
r. $(A \cap B) - C = A \cap (B - C)$.

2-8. Use Venn diagrams to decide the answers to each of the following. Are two or more of the sets $(\widetilde{\tilde{A} \cup \tilde{B}}) \cup (A \widetilde{\cup} B)$ and $(\tilde{A} \cap \tilde{B}) \cup (B \cap A)$ and $(\tilde{A} \cup B) \cap (\tilde{B} \cup A)$ the same set? Consider the sets A, $\tilde{A}$, B, $\tilde{B}$, $B - A$, $A - B$, S, $A \cap B$ and $A \cup B$. Which one is the same as the set $A \cap (\tilde{A} \cup B)$? Which one is the same as $(A \cap \tilde{B}) \cup (A \cap B)$? Which is $\tilde{A} \cup [(A \cup B) \cap (A \cup \tilde{B})]$? (The answers are revealed in the wording of one of the problems at the end of Chapter 3.)

2-9. Is $[A \cup (B \cap C)] - (\tilde{B} \cap C) = \{A - [(B \cap \tilde{C}) \cup (\tilde{B} \cap \tilde{C})]\} \cup \{B \cap C\}$ true? Use a Venn diagram. (The answer is yes.)

2-10. Suppose $\#$ is defined so that $A \# B$ means $(B - A) \cup (A - B)$. Then is $H \# J = J \# H$ true?
Is $H \# (J \# K) = (H \# J) \# K$ true?
Is $H \# (J \cup K) = (H \# J) \cup (H \# K)$ true?
Is $H \# (J \cap K) = (H \# J) \cap (H \# K)$ true?
Is $H \cup (J \# K) = (H \cup J) \# (H \cup K)$ true?
Is $H \cap (J \# K) = (H \cap J) \# (H \cap K)$ true?
(Answer: only three are true.)

2-11. Draw a Venn diagram and shade the "true" point set for each of the statements below. Are some of the statements equivalent or inconsistent? Is some statement true in every condition or false in every condition? Is there a statement which implies one or more of the others?

a. If we can, then we should.

b. If we should or can, then we cannot.

c. We should and cannot if and only if we should not or can.

d. We should or cannot if and only if we cannot and should not.

2-12. Go back to Section 2-6 of this chapter and translate Statements II and III into point set notation as was done for Statement I in the text. Draw their Venn diagrams *before* you take another look at the Figures 2-7. What is the relationship, if any, between Statements II and III?

2-13. For the *first three* statements below answer the same questions which were asked in Question 2-11, using Venn diagrams, of course. Now do this for *all* of the statements below, and happy landings.

a. If it is true that you laugh, and cry or hiccup, then it is true that you laugh and cry, or hiccup.

b. You laugh, or you cry and hiccup, *if and only if* you laugh or cry, and hiccup.

c. You laugh, and cry or don't hiccup, *if and only if* you laugh and don't cry, or laugh and don't hiccup.

d. *If* it is true that you laugh or don't cry if and only if you laugh and hiccup, *then* it is true that you cry, or laugh and hiccup.

e. It is true that, if you laugh and cry and don't hiccup, then you hiccup, or you cry and don't laugh, *if and only if* it is true that you laugh and don't cry, or cry and don't laugh.

2-14. Suppose that the statement, "Either the killey-loo bird does not like the wind in his face and flies backward, or he either flies backward or gets airsick," is a true statement *if and only if* the statement, "The killey-loo bird does not fly backward and, if he gets airsick, then he likes the wind in his face," is also a true statement. After sketching some appropriate Venn diagrams, answer the following questions. Does the killey-loo bird fly backward? Does he like the wind in his face? Does he get airsick? In your work, do *not* assume that his liking the wind in his face would prevent him from flying backward. (The answers are no, yes, and yes, respectively.)

2-15. The Rackear record company took a statistical sample of 100 teenagers to determine their tastes in three kinds of popular music. It was found that seventy liked high rock: assorted screams, grunts, and moans embedded in a clangor of blasting instruments, accompanied by the rattling of ash cans in broken glass. Also, seventy liked low rock: monotonous pounding punctuated by love-sick sobs usually lasting through several agonies of three fits each. Sixty-eight teenagers liked rock bottom: random noise turned up to a brain-battering volume. Fifty liked both high and low rock, fifty-five liked high rock and rock bottom, and forty-five craved low rock and rock bottom. Only two teenagers did not enjoy any of these kinds of music, apparently being malcontents who are *never* satisfied. How many of the teenagers were hardy enough to take all three kinds of assault?

2–16. You contract for an insurance company to provide monthly income to your parents for as long as either or both shall live. You want them to receive monthly incomes as follows.

Survivors	Monthly Income
Only mother alive	$100
Only father alive	200
Both alive	250

For this you will pay the premium to the company in a lump sum. For each dollar of monthly income the company charges you joint-life premium rates as follows.

Single Life	Rate per Dollar	Joint Life	Rate per Dollar
Mother	$204.50	Mother or Father	$127.60
Father	152.30		

What total premium must you pay the company? (Answer: $44,530.) Now go back and explain the error in your reasoning which caused that $31,900 figure to appear somewhere in your first attempt to solve this problem.

2–17. The personnel department of the Eiffel N. Love & Whee R. Keeping Company classifies all employees according to sex, education, department, and age. It is found that they employ the following.
Only 20 male collegiate office workers under forty years old,
Only 32 male collegiate office workers,
Only 30 male collegiates under forty years old,
Only 35 male office workers under forty years old,
Only 45 collegiate office workers under forty years old,
Only 59 male collegiates,
Only 65 males under forty years old,
Only 67 collegiate office workers,
Only 96 office workers under forty years old,
Exactly 39 workers who are males only,
Only 134 males,

Exactly 40 workers who are collegiates only,
Only 144 collegiates,
Only 153 office workers,
Only 153 under forty years old,
Only 30 who are none of these.

How many employees are there, how many are *only* college people under forty, and how many are male office workers? (Answers: 336, 10, and 48.)

2–18. Explain why each subdivision is a refinement of itself. Explain why no subdivision is a subdivision of itself. Explain why the right diagram of Figure 2–10a is not a partition of the set A. Is A covered by $\{B_1, B_2, \ldots, B_8\}$? Give two reasons why the set of circles in Figure 2–10b is not a partition of the set A. If B is a partition of the point set A, and C is a refinement of B, why is C a partition of A but not a refinement of A? (The wording of the definitions in the text is the key to each question, of course.)

2–19. List five ways the set of all citizens of the U.S. can be partitioned. How can each be refined? Give an example of a cross-partition of two of your partitions. Is this cross-partition also a refinement? Of which of your partitions is it a refinement?

2–20. An IBM card has eighty columns, each column having space for twelve punched holes. If each company employee is represented by exactly one card in a stack of IBM cards, into how many subsets can we partition the set of all employees by sorting on column one? Does each column represent a way we can partition the set of all employees? (Assume each column has information punched into it.) Do columns one and two together represent a cross-partition? What is the maximum number of cells possible in this cross-partition? In the three-partition cross-partition represented by the first three columns?

2–21. Review the Topheavy Corporation example in the text. Draw a diagram representing the partition {loyal men, loyal women, spies}. Now refine each cell of this partition into four subsets: manufacturing, sales, office, and management. Draw a Venn diagram (like that in Figure 2–11b) for this refinement, and also draw the tree diagram for it. Since you used "pie" diagrams, your refinement is arranged differently from the refinement in Figure 2–11b, even though you have the same cells. Notice that superimposing your partition diagram on the left one of Figure 2–11b does *not* give a pie diagram which represents the cross-partitioning of the partition X: {manufacturing, sales, office, management} with the partition Y: {loyal men, loyal women, spies}. Observe Figure 2–12b and then sketch diagrams representing partitions X and Y so that, when they are superimposed, the resulting diagram *does* show both partitions and the cross-partition.

2–22. The Halcyon Corporation has asset-account balances as follows.

Current Assets:

Cash in Bank and in Imprest Funds	$ 1,000,000
Accounts and Notes Receivable, less	
Allowance for Doubtful Accounts	10,000,000
Accrued Interest Receivable	20,000
Marketable Securities (at Cost)	500,000
Inventories, less Allowance for Drop in	
Market Value	20,000,000
Prepaid Rent and Insurance	110,000
Prepaid Federal Taxes	3,000,000

Investments:

90% Equity in Brown Co., a Subsidiary	2,500,000
Securities Sinking Fund for Bond	
Retirement, less Allowance for	
Drop in Market Value of Securities	9,000,000
Land Currently Unused	100,000

Fixed Assets:

Machinery and Equipment, less	
Amortization for Depreciation	23,300,000
Buildings, less Amortization for	
Depreciation	10,000,000
Land	2,000,000

Intangible Assets:

Goodwill (Premium Paid on Purchase of	
Brown Co.)	5,000,000
Original Organization and Incorporation Costs	700,000
Patents at Cost, less Amortization for	
Expired Life	1,400,000

Deferred Costs:

Research Costs, less Amortization for Expired	
Portion of Expected Life	1,300,000
Discount on Sales of Our Bonds,	
less Amortization	70,000
Total Assets	$90,000,000

Sketch a pie diagram which shows the subdivision A: {current assets, investments, fixed assets, intangible assets, deferred costs} of these eighteen accounts. This kind of diagram is often found in a corporation's annual report to its stockholders. Make the eighteen pie-diagram areas roughly proportional to their account balances. Sketch the subdivision B: {deductible-allowance accounts, amortizable accounts, other accounts} of the eighteen accounts. List the accounts in each cell of the cross–partition of A and B. List the accounts in each cell of partition C: {quick assets,* assets which would

---

*Cash or other assets which could be quickly and conveniently converted to cash in the event of an emergency.

be sold *only* in the event of complete liquidation and dissolution of the corporation, assets which have no sales value, all other assets}. Is the set of all eighteen accounts a cross–partition of two of the partitions *A*, *B*, and *C*? Of all three?

2–23. You are auditing the books of the Scrooge, Scrounge, and Scourge Loan Company. In order to judge the reasonableness of their estimated allowance for uncollectible notes, you are going to "age" their Notes Receivable account as of December 31, the end of their fiscal year. That is, you will obtain a list of all the promissory

Date of Note	Maker	Maturity Value	Maturity Date	Collateral or Cosigners
Nov. 30	Miss Melody Mellow	$ 200	Jan. 31	Her brother, Marsh
Oct. 10	Piercepulp Dental Drill Co.	325	Dec. 10	Dr. Gimlet V. Piercepulp and wife, Dentyne
Oct. 15	Cosmo Thudbottom	50	Dec. 25	None
Sept. 1	Lemuel Logos, Ltd.	575	Oct. 1	Watered Stocks, Soggy Bonds
Sept. 22	Mr. Mongoose N. Snake	75	Nov. 22	None
Dec. 1	Smog Watchers, Inc.	300	Feb. 1	100 cases of Murine
Dec. 1	Piltdown Genuine Antiques	250	Jan. 15	The proprietor, Simeon Jawbone
Oct. 31	Rick R. Mortis Funeral Parlor	1,000	Jan. 31	Go now—pay later Contracts
Sept. 25	Miss Impudence N. Sass	100	Oct. 25	None
Nov. 15	Iva Icelip	25	Dec. 15	3 million popsicle wrappers
Sept. 12	Kent Sleepnights	190	Nov. 12	Ian Somnia
Oct. 1	Plastered Pussycat Billiard & Pool Emporium	700	Jan. 14	526 pool cues (all chalked)
Oct. 10	The Svelte Feedbag Restaurant	200	Dec. 10	800 bags of oats
Dec. 31	Zergabel Mfg. Co.	750	Feb. 28	3000 zergabels
Oct. 5	Vincent van Goof	75	Dec. 5	None
Sept. 1	Mr. Lithium Redburn	400	Oct. 20	Mr. Barry M. Greenflame

notes they held which were outstanding at the end of the fiscal year, verify it against the company's records, and then partition the set of all these outstanding notes receivable into the subdivision D: {not due yet on December 31, overdue less than thirty days, overdue at least thirty days but less than sixty days, overdue at least sixty days but less than ninety days, overdue at least ninety days}. The list on page 45 was taken from the notes–receivable ledger. Assume the company does not give loans of more than six months duration. Rule off six columns on a sheet of paper, write "Maker" atop the first column and label the other five columns for the five sets in partition D. List the names of the makers (debtors) in the first column in an order which will partition them vertically into the cells of partition E: {collateral, cosigner, neither}. On your paper write each maturity value opposite the maker in the proper column. Where are the cells of the cross-partition of D and E, and how many are there? Represent this cross-partition with a tree diagram. What is the *maximum* number of cells we could have in it by rearranging maturity dates? Answer this with a tree diagram. What does the number 5×3 represent?

2-24. Our mail order house used to automatically mail free catalogues annually to all addresses on its permanent master mailing list and found each year that one or more orders were received from 30 per cent of these addresses (not the same 30 per cent each year). As of the catalogue mail-out a year ago, we adopted the permanent policy that catalogues are mailed only to those addresses on the permanent master mailing list from which orders are received during the preceding year. Now we scan our sales records for this last year and find that half of those addresses which got catalogues a year ago have since produced orders. Of course, some addresses not getting new catalogues a year ago have since ordered from us. If 29 per cent of *all* the addresses will receive the new catalogue which we are now about to mail out, what per cent of the permanent master mailing list got no catalogues last year and will receive no catalogues this year? Support your answer with the appropriate Venn diagram.

chapter three

Probability Space and
Boolean Algebra

So far, we have mentioned some of the meanings we want our primitive notions of "set," "member," and "universal set" to have, as well as some interpretations to be avoided. We have also defined some terms, such as ∪, ∩, and ⊆, which we employ in order to make it easier to talk about these primitive notions. Moreover, some experience in applying these notions and terms is under our belts now. But we have yet to discover and list in an orderly manner the basic properties and principles which govern not only the applications of sets but also the obtaining of information from models which are constructed from sets. Obviously, if we are to hang our thinking upon a framework of sets, we ought to organize and know the basic properties common to all sets and set operations. In Section 3–1 of this chapter we shall derive and list many of these properties. Proceeding carefully, we shall justify each property from some or all of the *primitive notions* as well as any other properties which we may have already discovered and placed on our list.

Of course, a mere reading ahead along the list will *inform* you of the properties, but this behavior will do nothing to *develop your understanding* of sets. Instead, you should pause and construct a careful justification for each property on the list *as you come to it*. The justification (called a proof) is constructed from all notions and properties already on the list. This behavior will develop your knack for handling sets, will probably amuse you, and will force you to think precisely. And when all is said and done, a system of precise thought is what mathematics really is—it is not just the manipulation of symbols. (Mindless manipulators often find that their labors lead to solid gold broom closets.) Students who neglect careful understanding at the beginning of a mathematical system and impatiently bypass it in favor of subsequent topics in the system deceive themselves into thinking that their progress is thus more rapid along their route. But mathematical knowledge is cumulative, and a failure to understand fundamentals compounds itself into a complete failure later on. Initial understanding is essential.

As I have said, systems of logic, such as the plane geometry of Euclid, our number system, the system of double-entry bookkeeping and the physical mechanics of Isaac Newton, are based upon one or more basic notions or starting assumptions; one then proceeds to reason about the subjects of these notions and assumptions. The results of such reasoning are listed in the form of true statements, which in mathematics are called *theorems*. For example, all the statements you were asked to explain in Questions 2–2b, 2–6 and 2–7 are theorems. The truth of each of these follows from and depends on our *set*, *member*, and *universal set* notions, as well as the definitions we have made concerning them. The most important of these theorems will be stated again below. I will give proofs for some of them. You will give proofs for the others, in order to develop your ability, as well as a feeling for sets.

Each theorem is an "If . . . , then . . ." statement or an "if and only if" statement (which is just a two–way "if–then" statement). To prove it, you give an argument to show that its conclusion (the "then . . ." part) follows from its hypothesis (the "If . . .," part) plus the basic notions and starting assumptions which apply plus (if convenient) other theorems which have been previously proved from these basic notions and assumptions. You may use Venn diagrams as an aid to your imagination while trying to understand why a theorem is true, but you *may not* incorporate them into your arguments in any way. The mistake you would be making would be the "proof by example" fallacy. One who points to a bald man and claims this shows that all men are bald is making this kind of mistake. Similarly, when you refer to a diagram and claim that *all* sets (even sets which are not point sets!) have a property possessed by the sets in the diagram, you are also committing this kind of error.

3–1. THEOREMS WHICH ARE CONSEQUENCES OF THE NOTIONS OF SET, MEMBER, AND UNIVERSAL SET

Let us, then, take our first steps into the system of logic for sets. Most of the steps will be extremely easy for you, but there are some which will challenge you and require more than just a few minutes of thought. I will present a proof of the first theorem for you, but remember that the more you prove for yourself, the better will be your understanding, and the better will be your bridge to more advanced topics.

Theorem 1. *If X is a set and Y is a set, then there exists one and only one set $X \cup Y$. Furthermore, $X \subseteq X \cup Y$ and $Y \subseteq X \cup Y$.*

To prove there is a unique set $X \cup Y$ we must show (1) that there is a meaningful definition which we would want for $X \cup Y$, (2) that there is at least one member of $X \cup Y$, and (3) that there is *only* one set which has the properties mentioned in the definition of $X \cup Y$. We proceed as follows.

There exist a set X and a set Y.

(Because we are given this information in the theorem's hypothesis.)

Hence, there exist meaningful definitions for X and for Y.

(Because *meaningful definition* is one of Chapter 1's "properties every set has.")

Then, "The set such that a thing is a member of it if and only if that thing is a member of X or Y," is meaningful.

(Because, if "member of X" is meaningful and "member of Y" is meaningful, then "member of X or Y" is also meaningful, according to our notion of the term "or.")

Hence, we have shown (1) a meaningful definition for $X \cup Y$.

Now X has at least one member.

(Because this is one of Chapter 1's "properties every set has.")

The member of X is also a member of $X \cup Y$.

(Because of the way we defined $X \cup Y$.)

Hence, we have shown (2) that $X \cup Y$ has at least one member.

Now there cannot be two sets (say A and B) which satisfy the definition of $X \cup Y$.

(Because, if there were two such sets A and B, then $A \neq B$, and some member of A would not be in B or vice versa, which is the same as saying that some member of X or Y would not be in X or Y or vice versa.)

Hence, we have shown (3) that there is *only* one set $X \cup Y$.

The next thing we are asked to show is that $X \subseteq X \cup Y$.

Each member of X is also in $X \cup Y$.

(Because of the definition of $X \cup Y$.)

Then $X \subseteq X \cup Y$.

(Because of the definition of the term *subset*.)

We show that $Y \subseteq X \cup Y$ in the same manner. This completes the proof of Theorem 1.

Theorem 2. *If X is a set and Y is a set and some member of X also belongs to Y, then there exists one and only one set $X \cap Y$. Furthermore, $X \cap Y \subseteq X$ and $X \cap Y \subseteq Y$.*

Theorem 3. *If X is a set and $X \neq S$, then there exists one and only one set $S - X$. Moreover, $X \cup (S - X) = S$.*

Arguments for Theorems 2 and 3 parallel the argument given for Theorem 1. You should stop reading for a moment and give the arguments to show that both Theorems 2 and 3 follow from our fundamental notions and definitions.

Theorem 4. *If X is a set and Y is a set such that either $X \cup Y = Y$ or $X \cap Y = X$, then $X \subseteq Y$.*

If $X \cup Y = Y$, then each member of X or Y is in Y; hence each member of X is in Y, and this means that $X \subseteq Y$. If $X \cap Y = X$, then each member of X is in X and Y; hence each member of X is in Y, and this means that $X \subseteq Y$. We have therefore shown that if either $X \cup Y = Y$ or $X \cap Y = X$, then $X \subseteq Y$.

Theorem 5. *If $X \subseteq Y$, then $X \cup Y = Y$ and $X \cap Y = X$.*

Try your hand at proving this one. It is as easy as Theorem 4.

Theorem 6. *Union and intersection are commutative.* That is, if X is a set and Y is a set, then $X \cup Y = Y \cup X$ and, if X intersects Y, then $X \cap Y = Y \cap X$.*

Theorem 7. *Union and intersection are associative. That is, if X is a set and Y is a set and Z is a set, then $X \cup (Y \cup Z) = (X \cup Y) \cup$*

---

*The terms *commutative, associative, distributive, idempotent, identity,* and *unique,* which appear in the statements of Theorems 6, 7, 8, 9, 10, 11, 13, 21, and 22, are names for properties which crop up in many other mathematical systems. Hence each is a generalization which applies often in mathematics. If you develop a careful understanding of them here, it will greatly aid your understanding in many other areas of mathematics.

Z and, if X, Y, and Z have a common part, then $X \cap (Y \cap Z)$
$= (X \cap Y) \cap Z$.

Both Theorems 6 and 7 follow from the meanings of the words "or"
and "and" used in the definitions of union and intersection. That is,
"X or Y" means the same as "Y or X," and "X and Y" means the same as
"Y and X"; while "X, or Y or Z" means the same as "X or Y, or Z," and
"X, and Y and Z" means the same as "X and Y, and Z."

*Theorem 8. Intersection is distributive over union. That is, if either $X \cap Y$
exists or $X \cap Z$ exists, then $X \cap (Y \cup Z) = (X \cap Y) \cup
(X \cap Z)$.*

This relationship can also be shown with a play on the words "or"
and "and." Each member of $X \cap (Y \cup Z)$ is a member of X and a
member of Y or Z, which means the same as being a member of X and Y
or a member of X and Z, and this is what is meant by membership in
$(X \cap Y) \cup (X \cap Z)$. Hence, each member of $X \cap (Y \cup Z)$ is also a
member of $(X \cap Y) \cup (X \cap Z)$. Now we reverse this argument to show
that each member of $(X \cap Y) \cup (X \cap Z)$ is also a member of
$X \cap (Y \cup Z)$. Pause now and do this. Hence, $X \cap (Y \cup Z)$ must be the
same set as $(X \cap Y) \cup (X \cap Z)$ because they have the same membership. In case there is no set $X \cap Y$ or no set $X \cap Z$, then we incorporate
into our argument the fact that $A \cup B$ is defined to be A in case B does not
exist. Thus, if $X \cap Y$ does not exist, then $X \cap (Y \cup Z) = (X \cap Y) \cup
(X \cap Z)$ becomes $X \cap (Y \cup Z) = X \cap Z$.

*Theorem 9. Union is distributive over intersection. That is, $X \cup (Y \cap Z)$
$= (X \cup Y) \cap (X \cup Z)$. (Existence of $Y \cap Z$ is not necessary.)*

This is not as easy to prove as Theorem 8. We can show that each
member of $(X \cup Y) \cap (X \cup Z)$ is also a member of $X \cup (Y \cap Z)$ by
classifying the membership of $(X \cup Y) \cap (X \cup Z)$ into five cases. Each
member of $(X \cup Y) \cap (X \cup Z)$ is a member of X or Y and X or Z. This
means each member is either a member of only X, or of only X and Z,
or of only Y and X, or of only Y and Z, or of X and Y and Z. In each of
these five cases the member will also belong to X, or Y and Z, which
means it belongs to the set $X \cup (Y \cap Z)$. Hence, each member of
$(X \cup Y) \cap (X \cup Z)$ is also a member of $X \cup (Y \cap Z)$. Now we must
show the converse: that each member of $X \cup (Y \cap Z)$ is also a member
of $(X \cup Y) \cap (X \cup Z)$. Pause now and show this yourself. (You can break
$X \cup (Y \cap Z)$ into three cases.)

*Theorem 10. Union and intersection are each idempotent. That is, if X is
a set, then $X \cup X = X$ and $X \cap X = X$.*

Since every set is a subset of itself, then $X \subseteq X$. This satisfies the hypothesis (the "if" part) of Theorem 5, so the conclusion (the "then" part) of Theorem 5 gives us what we are trying to prove: $X \cup X = X$ and $X \cap X = X$.

Theorem 11. The set S is an identity element for the $\cap$ operation. That is, if X is a set, then $X \cap S = X$.

Show how Theorem 5 can be used on this one. And now prove it again *without* the aid of Theorem 5.

Theorem 12. If $X \cup Y = X \cup Z$ and $X \cap Y = X \cap Z$, then $Y = Z$.

This one is a good one for you. Prove it by showing that each member of Y is a member of Z and that each member of Z is a member of Y.

All spaces have the properties stated in the conclusions of these twelve theorems, because every space has all properties which are inherent in our notions of *set, member,* and *universal set.*

3–2. AXIOMS FOR PROBABILITY SPACE

Let us now confine our attention to only those spaces which exhibit a certain collection of four properties which I have in mind. Such properties are called *axioms* by the mathematician. He thinks of them as "fundamental assumptions" when he uses them, because he assumes that the space he is considering has all the fundamental properties called for by the axioms. The reason we are so interested in the particular axioms I am going to list is that every model which is used to solve a probability problem is a space which has these properties. Spaces which satisfy the following four axioms are called *probability spaces,* or *sample spaces,* or *sample description spaces,* or *sigma spaces.*

Axiom I. *There exists a collection D, each member of which is a subset of S. (D is called a probability domain on the space S if it satisfies all four axioms.)*

Axiom II. *If the set X is a member of D and the set Y is a member of D and $X \cap Y$ exists, then $X \cap Y$ is also a member of D.*

Axiom III. *The set $\emptyset$ has the property that it is a subset of each member of D.*

Axiom IV. *The set $\emptyset$ has the property that, if X is a member of D, then the set $(S - X) \cup \emptyset$ is also a member of D. (The set $(S - X) \cup \emptyset$ is called the complement of X, and we shall denote it by X'.)*

Figures 3–1 and 3–2 show examples of spaces which satisfy all four of our axioms. Hence, our axiom set is not trivial. In the rest of the text there will be presented many examples of spaces S with their collections D of sets. Some will satisfy all four axioms and some will not, depending on the idea to be illustrated.

It is my experience in classroom teaching that many students fail to understand Axiom I and are unable to distinguish between members of D and members of S. Bear in mind that D is a collection of sets. (That is, D is a collection of one or more sets.) Each member of D is a *subset* of S and therefore cannot be a *member* of S. The following example satisfies Axiom I and should aid your understanding of Axiom I. Let S denote the U. S. electorate, the set of all eligible U. S. voters. We will suppose that

The members of D are point sets in the Venn diagram to the right. D is the collection $\{S, \phi, X, Y, Z, X', Y', Z'\}$. These are the shaded point sets illustrated below.

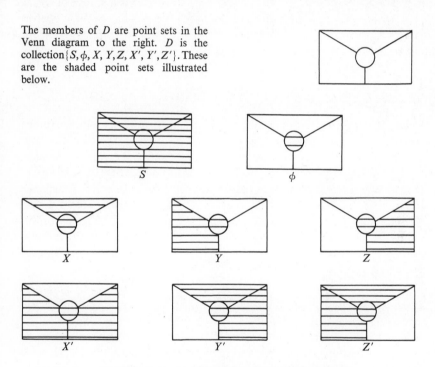

FIGURE 3-1. An Example of a Collection D Which Satisfies All Four Axioms (To prevent the boundary points of the above sets from contradicting our axioms, we can either omit all boundary points from S, or we can include them all in each member of D.)

Consider the Venn diagram to the right.
Let D denote the collection $\{S, \phi, A, A',$
$B, B',\ A \cap B,\ A \cap B',\ A' \cap B,\ A' \cap B',$
$A \cup B,\quad A \cup B',\quad A' \cup B,\quad A' \cup B',$
$(A \cap B) \cup (A' \cap B'), (A \cap B') \cup (A' \cap B)\}.$
The sixteen members of D are represented
by the shaded point sets below.

S

ϕ

A

B

B'

A'

$A \cap B$

$A \cap B'$

$A' \cap B$

$A' \cap B'$

$A \cup B$

$A \cup B'$

$A' \cup B$

$A' \cup B'$

$(A \cap B) \cup (A' \cap B')$

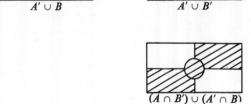

$(A \cap B') \cup (A' \cap B)$

FIGURE 3-2. Another Example of a Space
Satisfying All Four Axioms (Omit
all boundary points of each set
from each member of D.)

there are only four U. S. political parties—the Democrats, Republicans, Socialists, and Prohibitionists—and that each eligible U. S. voter is a card-carrying member of one and only one of them. Let D denote the set of all U. S. political parties. Since each party is a set (of people) and D is a collection of parties, then D is a collection of sets. D has only four members—the four parties. S, on the other hand, is a collection of people and has more than 100 million members—the voters. No member of D is a member of S because no party is a voter. But each member of D is a subset of S, because each of the four parties is a subset of the electorate (according to our supposition above). The distinction between D and S is obvious in this example. Notice also that D covers S, and S is not a member of D. Of course, this example satisfies Axioms I and II but not the last two axioms. (Show this.)

The example illustrated in Figure 3–1 does satisfy all four axioms. Observe that this S is a set of *points* and has infinitely many members. But D is a set of *sets* and has only eight members, each of which is a *subset* of S but not a *member* of S. The distinction between D and S is obvious in this example too.

Axiom I requires that S contains each member of D as a subset, but we are not told whether S is also a member of D. Theorem 20, a consequence of the axioms, settles the question. Axiom I also fails to tell us whether D covers S. (See Question 3–6.)

Deciding whether a collection D_1 of sets satisfies Axiom II can be a chore if D_1 has many members. For example, if the sets $(A \cap B) \cup (A' \cap B')$ and $(A \cap B') \cup (A' \cap B)$ in Figure 3–2 had been omitted from the list of the sixteen members of D, it would have been easy to overlook this omission and not to realize that the example would fail to satisfy Axiom II. The sets $A' \cup B$ and $A \cup B'$ would have no common part in D and the sets $A \cup B$ and $A' \cup B'$ would have no common part in D.

Axiom III guarantees us that if X and Y are sets which are members of D, then X and Y have a common part —each member of $\emptyset$ is in $X \cap Y$. Notice that Axiom III does not say that $\emptyset$ is a subset of every *set*; it says that $\emptyset$ is a subset of every set *which is a member of D*.

We mentioned before that there are many people who are willing to use such words as, "E is the empty set," when they really mean that there is a meaningful set–definition for E, but nothing qualifies as a member (i.e., there is no such set E). Some people like to carry this legal fiction a step or two further and say, "The empty set is a subset of every set, and therefore each pair of sets has a common part." They then reserve some symbol such as E to denote "the empty set" and incorporate it into Boolean algebra, which is the algebra of sets developed by the Englishman George Boole. The resulting algebra is much more useful and esthetically pleasing because each pair of sets comes complete with common part. You will observe, however, that our Axiom III achieves precisely the same results for us, and we do not have to pay the price of nonexistence. *All* of our sets have membership, including $\emptyset$. This is inherent in *our* notion of *set*. (You might say that we do not have to Boole around with an "empty set.")

We do have to be careful when setting up a mathematical model for a probability problem to have a set $\emptyset$ which is a subset of every other set in our probability domain D. We usually sweep all the possible outcomes of the experiment (the possible outcomes will be the members of S) which we consider to be insignificant into the set $\emptyset$ and make sure to include them in each event ("event" is going to mean "member of D"). In the duel problem of Chapter one, for instance, we would consider as insignificant a possible outcome in which both men die of fright. We have neglected to consider this kind of possibility until now. We will want to assign the value of zero to the probability that some possible outcome in the set $\emptyset$ will occur.

Notice that Axiom III does not mention whether $\emptyset$ is a member of D. This question is settled in Theorem 18.

Axiom IV introduces another kind of complementary set. The *complement* of the set X (if X is in D) is $(S - X) \cup \emptyset$, but the complement of X *with respect to* S is merely $S - X$. We are guaranteed by Axiom IV that each member of $\emptyset$ is also a member of X', but we do not know from Axiom IV *alone* whether some or all of the members of $\emptyset$ are also members of $S - X$.

When deciding for some collection D_1 of sets whether it satisfies all four axioms, one must be careful to determine not only that each member of D_1 has a complement, but also that its complement is actually in D_1 according to D_1's definition. For example, if $A \cup B'$ were omitted from the sixteen-member list of members of D in Figure 3–2, then $A' \cap B$ would have no complement in that D. It is true that there would *exist* a set $[S - (A' \cap B)] \cup \emptyset$, namely $A \cup B'$, but it would not be in D! In this case D would fail to satisfy Axiom IV. We shall see from Theorems 19, 20, and 23 that, for each probability domain, S and $\emptyset$ are complements of each other.

Before proceeding, we should show that each axiom is *independent* of the other three, which means that no axiom follows from the others and should therefore be called a theorem. Such repetition among axioms should be eliminated because the list of basic properties we want to assume as axioms should be as *short* as possible, thereby minimizing the risk that a subtle contradiction-between-properties lurks unnoticed in our system of axioms. Moreover, it is easier to decide whether an example of a space satisfies a list of axioms if the list is short. We can show independence by giving for each axiom an example of a space which does not satisfy it, but which does satisfy the other three axioms.

The following shows that Axiom I does not follow from the other three. An example of a collection D_1 of sets which satisfies only Axioms II, III, and IV can be constructed from the sets shown in Figure 3–1 as well as $\{S\}$, the set* whose only member is S. Let D_1 denote the collection $\{S, \emptyset, X, Y, Z, X', Y', Z', S \cup \{S\}, \emptyset \cup \{S\}, X \cup \{S\}, Y \cup \{S\}, Z \cup \{S\}, X' \cup \{S\}, Y' \cup \{S\}, Z' \cup \{S\}\}$. Now D_1 does not satisfy Axiom I because none of the last eight members is a subset of S. But D_1 does satisfy Axiom II. (The common part of X and $X \cup \{S\}$, for example, would be X, which is in D_1. The common part of $X \cup \{S\}$ and $X' \cup \{S\}$ would be $\emptyset \cup \{S\}$, which is in D_1. The common part of $Y' \cup \{S\}$ and $Z' \cup \{S\}$ would be $X \cup \{S\}$, which is in D_1.) Axiom III is satisfied because, if $\emptyset$ is a subset of each member of the D of Figure 3–1, then $\emptyset$ must also be a subset of each member of D_1. Axiom IV is satisfied by D_1, because each member of D_1 has a complement which is also in D_1. (For example, $S \cup \{S\}$ has $\emptyset$ as its complement, $\emptyset \cup \{S\}$ has S as its complement and $X \cup \{S\}$ has X' as its complement.)

Axiom II does not follow from Axioms I, III, and IV because of the following space, which satisfies all axioms except II. Let D_2 denote the two-member collection whose only members are the sets $\{1, 2\}$ and $\{2, 3\}$. That is, D_2 is $\{\{1, 2\}, \{2, 3\}\}$. S is the set $\{1, 2, 3\}$ and $\emptyset$ is the set $\{2\}$. (Observe that S and $\emptyset$ are not members of D.) Axiom I is satisfied because D_2 is a collection of sets, and each is a subset of S (both $\{1, 2\}$ and $\{2, 3\}$ are subsets of $\{1, 2, 3\}$). Axiom II is not satisfied because the common part $\{2\}$ of the two members of D_2 is not a member of D_2. Axiom III is satisfied because there is a set $\emptyset$, namely $\{2\}$, which is a subset of each member of D_2. Axiom IV is satisfied because $(S - \{1, 2\}) \cup \emptyset$, which is $\{2, 3\}$, is a member of D_2 and $(S - \{2, 3\}) \cup \emptyset$, which is $\{1, 2\}$, is a member of D_2.

Axiom III is independent because the collection D_3: $\{\{a, b\}, \{a\}, \{b\}\}$, for which $S = \{a, b\}$, satisfies all but the third axiom. Axioms I and II are obviously satisfied,† but III is not satisfied because there is no set which is a subset of each member of D_3. Axiom IV is satisfied because, if we let $\emptyset$ mean $\{b\}$, then $\{a, b\}' = \{b\}$, $\{a\}' = \{b\}$ and $\{b\}' = \{a, b\}$.

---

*S is different from $\{S\}$. Remember that $\{S\}$ is the set whose only *member* is the universal set S. Now consider the set $S \cup \{S\}$. Observe that S is a *subset* of $S \cup \{S\}$ and S is also a *member* of $S \cup \{S\}$! However, $S \cup \{S\}$ is not a subset of S because S is not a member of S.

†There is no $\{a\} \cap \{b\}$, but this is not a contradiction to Axiom II.

Axiom IV is independent because the space D_4: $\{\{0, 1, 2, 3\}, \{0, 1\},$
$\{0, 2\}, \{0, 3\}, \{0\}\}$ satisfies only our first three axioms. This time you may
have the pleasure of explaining why and why not.

3-3. THEOREMS WHICH ARE CONSEQUENCES OF ALL FOUR AXIOMS AS WELL AS OF THE NOTIONS OF SET, MEMBER, AND UNIVERSAL SET

Now that you grasp fully the meaning of our four axioms, let us direct
our attention exclusively to those spaces S and collections D of sets which
satisfy all four of the axioms. That is, in the rest of the text we assume all
four axioms are true of each space we consider or mention.

*Theorem 13. The set $\emptyset$ is an identity element for the $\cup$ operation. That
is, if the set A is a member of D, then $A \cup \emptyset = A$.*

Since A is in D by hypothesis, then $\emptyset \subseteq A$, according to Axiom III.
Then the hypothesis of Theorem 5 is satisfied, and its conclusion says
that $\emptyset \cup A = A$. Since $\cup$ is commutative according to Theorem 6,
$\emptyset \cup A = A \cup \emptyset$. After substitution between these last two equations we
can write $A \cup \emptyset = A$, which was to be proved.

Theorem 14. If A is a set which is a member of D, then $A \cap \emptyset = \emptyset$.

Theorem 15. If A is a set (not necessarily a member of D), *then $A \cup S = S$.*

These last two theorems are easy. Prove them before you continue.

Theorem 16. If A is a set which is a member of D, then $A \cap A' = \emptyset$.

Prove this one before you look at the argument for Theorem 17.

Theorem 17. If A is a set which is a member of D, then $A \cup A' = S$.

Since A is in D, then there exists a set A' in D according to Axiom IV.
Theorem 1 assures us that there exists one and only one set $A \cup A'$.
Since A' means $(S - A) \cup \emptyset$, which may also be written $\tilde{A} \cup \emptyset$, then
$A \cup A' = A \cup (\tilde{A} \cup \emptyset)$. Since $\cup$ is associative according to Theorem
7, the right–hand member of this equation may be changed to obtain
$A \cup A' = (A \cup \tilde{A}) \cup \emptyset$. But $A \cup \tilde{A} = S$, by Theorem 3. Hence our
equation becomes $A \cup A' = S \cup \emptyset$, which can be rewritten $A \cup A' =
\emptyset \cup S$ according to the commutative property of Theorem 6. Now
Theorem 15 tells us that $\emptyset \cup S$ is the same as S, so that we can substitute
in the last equation to obtain $A \cup A' = S$, the conclusion we have been
trying to show. The literature would shorten the above argument into
the following presentation.

A is in D.	(Hypothesis)
There is an A' in D.	(Axiom IV)
$A \cup A'$ exists.	(Theorem 1)
$A' = \bar{A} \cup \emptyset$.	(Definition of A' in Axiom IV)
$A \cup A' = A \cup (\bar{A} \cup \emptyset)$.	(Substitution)
$\quad\quad = (A \cup \bar{A}) \cup \emptyset$.	(Associative Property)
$\quad\quad = S \cup \emptyset$.	(Theorem 3 and Substitution)
$\quad\quad = \emptyset \cup S$.	(Commutative Property)
$A \cup A' = S$.	(Theorem 15)

This sort of postulate reasoning is discussed in Volume I of this series.

Theorem 18. *The set $\emptyset$ is a member of D.*

Try this one yourself before you read the following, which is one way Theorem 18 can be proved.

D has at least one member.	(Axiom I)
Let X denote a member of D.	
X' is in D.	(Axiom IV)
X intersects X'.	(Axiom III)
$X \cap X'$ exists.	(Theorem 2)
$X \cap X' = \emptyset$.	(Theorem 16)
$X \cap X'$ is in D.	(Axiom II)
Hence $\emptyset$ is in D.	(Substitution)

And now you are on your own. Prove the remaining twelve theorems yourself. Each is an entertaining little puzzle. Remember that on each theorem you may use *all* the results which precede it in order to prove it. Be sure to give a reason for each step in each proof.

Theorem 19. $\emptyset' = S$.

Theorem 20. *S is a member of D.*

Theorem 21. *$\emptyset$ is unique in D. That is, there are not two members $\emptyset_1$ and $\emptyset_2$ of D such that (1) both are subsets of each member of D, and (2) each member X of D has a complement $(S - X) \cup \emptyset_1$ in D and a complement $(S - X) \cup \emptyset_2$ in D.*

This proof is an example of an *indirect* argument. In the indirect kind of proof, you start by assuming the opposite of what you want to prove, and then you show that this leads to an absurdity (a contradiction of something you know is true). Hence, what you want to prove must be true.

Theorem 22. *S is unique in D. That is, there is no set S_2, different from the universal set S, such that (1) each member of D is also a subset of S_2, and (2) each member X of D has a complement $(S_2 - X) \cup \emptyset$ which is a member of D.*

Theorem 23. *No member of D has two complements.*

Theorem 24. *If A is a member of D, then* $(A')' = A$.

The trick on this one is to see which of the previous theorems can be applied.

Theorem 25. $S' = \emptyset$.

Theorem 26. *If X is a set and Y is a set, then* $S - (X \cup Y) = (S - X) \cap (S - Y)$ *and* $S - (X \cap Y) = (S - X) \cup (S - Y)$.

Theorem 27. *If A is a member of D and B is a member of D, then* $A' \cap B' = (A \cup B)'$ *and* $A' \cup B' = (A \cap B)'$. (These are de Morgan's Laws.)

Theorem 28. *If A is a member of D and B is a member of D, then* $A \cup B$ *is also a member of D.*

Theorem 29. *If there exists some member of D which is its own complement, then D is degenerate.*

Theorem 30. *If A is a member of D and B is a member of D such that* $A' = B'$, *then* $A = B$.

3–4. BOOLEAN ALGEBRA

These theorems plus the theorems in Question 3–14 form the basis of the algebra of sets, which, as we have seen, is called *Boolean algebra*. It is often used to show that two symbols stand for the same set. Suppose, for instance, that we are confronted by the symbol $A \cup (A' \cap B)$. This boils down to nothing more than the set $A \cup B$, and Boolean algebra may be used to show this as follows.

$$
\begin{aligned}
A \cup (A' \cap B) &= (A \cup A') \cap (A \cup B) &&\text{(Theorem 9)} \\
&= S \cap (A \cup B) &&\text{(Theorem 17)} \\
&= (A \cup B) \cap S &&\text{(Theorem 6)} \\
&= A \cup B &&\text{(Theorem 11)}
\end{aligned}
$$

Here is another example.

$$
\begin{aligned}
(A \cup B) \cap (A \cup B') &= A \cup (B \cap B') &&\text{(Theorem 9)} \\
&= A \cup \emptyset &&\text{(Theorem 16)} \\
&= A &&\text{(Theorem 13)}
\end{aligned}
$$

To illustrate a variety of possible steps, suppose A and B are members of D and that $A' = B$.

Then

$$
(A')' = B' \qquad\qquad\qquad \text{(Axiom IV)}
$$

$$A = B' \qquad \text{(Theorem 24)}$$
$$A \cap B = B' \cap B \qquad \text{(Axiom III)}$$
$$A \cap B = B \cap B' \qquad \text{(Theorem 6)}$$
$$A \cap B = \emptyset \qquad \text{(Theorem 16)}$$
$$(A \cap B)' = \emptyset' \qquad \text{(Axiom IV)}$$
$$A' \cup B' = \emptyset' \qquad \text{(Theorem 27)}$$
$$A' \cup B' = S \qquad \text{(Theorem 19)}$$

The expression $X \cap (Y_1 \cup Y_2 \cup Y_3 \cup Y_4)$ crops up in a certain kind of probability problem, and Boolean algebra is used as follows.

$$X \cap \{[Y_1] \cup [Y_2 \cup Y_3 \cup Y_4]\} = \{X \cap Y_1\} \cup \{X \cap [Y_2 \cup Y_3 \cup Y_4]\}$$
$$\text{(Theorem 8)}$$
$$= \{X \cap Y_1\} \cup \{X \cap [Y_2 \cup (Y_3 \cup Y_4)]\}$$
$$= \{X \cap Y_1\} \cup \{[X \cap Y_2] \cup [X \cap (Y_3 \cup Y_4)]\} \qquad \text{(Theorem 8)}$$
$$= \{[X \cap Y_1] \cup [X \cap Y_2]\} \cup \{X \cap (Y_3 \cup Y_4)\} \qquad \text{(Theorem 7)}$$
$$= \{[X \cap Y_1] \cup [X \cap Y_2]\} \cup \{[X \cap Y_3] \cup [X \cap Y_4]\}$$
$$\text{(Theorem 8)}$$
$$= (X \cap Y_1) \cup (X \cap Y_2) \cup (X \cap Y_3) \cup (X \cap Y_4)$$

The initial idea was that $Y_1 \cup Y_2 \cup Y_3 \cup Y_4$ means the same as $(Y_1) \cup (Y_2 \cup Y_3 \cup Y_4)$ or $(Y_1 \cup Y_2) \cup (Y_3 \cup Y_4)$ or $(Y_1 \cup Y_2 \cup Y_3) \cup (Y_4)$, and we chose the first of the three groupings for our start.

3-5. PROBABILITY PARTITIONS

In the probability problem which is referred to incidentally in the last Boolean algebra example, it happens that the sets Y_1, Y_2, Y_3, and Y_4 are somewhat like a four-cell partition of S. The sets fill up S (that is, $Y_1 \cup Y_2 \cup Y_3 \cup Y_4 = S$), but they fail to be mutually exclusive solely because each of Y_1, Y_2, Y_3, and Y_4 contains $\emptyset$ as a subset. The set $\emptyset$ is a subset of each of Y_1, Y_2, Y_3, and Y_4 because each is either a member of D or the union of some members of D. Since this type of thing, in which $\emptyset$ is a subset of each cell, is the one used in probability, we shall now introduce a modification of the partition definition—a kind of partition in which each cell will contain $\emptyset$ as a subset.

The statement that the sets X and Y are mutually-exclusive-except-for-$\emptyset$ means that X and Y are both members of some probability domain D whose $\cup$ identity element is $\emptyset$, and that $X \cap Y = \emptyset$. Observe that the sets $A \cap B$ and $A' \cap B'$ in Figure 3-2 are mutually exclusive except for $\emptyset$, but the sets A and B are not because $(A \cap B) - \emptyset$ exists and therefore $A \cap B$ is not $\emptyset$. Notice also that if two members of a probability domain are complements of each other, then they are mutually exclusive except for $\emptyset$.

The statement that the collection C of sets C_1, C_2, C_3, ..., C_n is a probability-partition-with-respect-to-D of the set X means that (1) *D is a probability domain and X is a member of D (X is usually S),* (2) *each member of C is either a member of D or the union of some members of D,* (3) *C fills up X, and* (4) *the members of C are mutually-exclusive-except-for-$\emptyset$* (that is, each two members of *C* are mutually-exclusive-except-for-$\emptyset$). For example, in Figure 3–2, the collection of sets $\{A \cap B, A' \cap B, B'\}$ is a probability–partition–with–respect–to–D of the set *S*, while the collection $\{A \cap B, A' \cap B, A' \cap B'\}$ is a probability–partition–with–respect–to–D of the set $A' \cup B$ (but not of the set *S*, because the three cells do not fill up *S*).

In Figure 2–10a, let *P* denote the center point of the circle. Let *S* denote the set of the interior points only of the sets B_1, B_2, ..., B_8, plus the point *P*. Let each of the sets B_1, B_2, ..., B_8 include the point *P*, but no other boundary point. Then there exists a probability domain *D*, *some* of whose members are $S, \{P\}, B_1, B_2, ..., B_8, B_1 \cup B_2, B_1 \cup B_3, ..., B_1 \cup B_2 \cup B_3,$ ..., etc. In this case $\emptyset = \{P\}$. Then the sets $\{B_1, B_2, ..., B_8\}$ form a *probability-partition-with-respect-to-D* of the set *S*, because they are mutually exclusive except for $\{P\}$; they fill up *S* and they are members of *D*. However, these eight sets would not form a *partition* of *S* because they are not mutually exclusive: *P* belongs to each.

The following theorem crops up in problems on "conditional" probabilities.

Theorem 31. *If* $\{B_1, B_2, ..., B_n\}$ *is a probability-partition-with-respect-to-D of the set S and the set A is a member of D, then* $A \cap (B_1 \cup B_2 \cup ... \cup B_n) = A = (A \cap B_1) \cup (A \cap B_2) \cup ... \cup (A \cap B_n)$ *and* $A \cup (B_1 \cap B_2 \cap ... \cap B_n) = A = (A \cup B_1) \cap (A \cup B_2) \cap ... \cap (A \cup B_n).$

Sketch a Venn diagram to illustrate this, and then use Boolean algebra to prove the theorem.

Questions

3–1. Some of the set theorems are similar to theorems about numbers. For example, the $X \cap (Y \cup Z) = (X \cap Y) \cup (X \cap Z)$ of Theorem 8 is like the $x \cdot (y + z) = (x \cdot y) + (x \cdot z)$ property of numbers, the $A \cup \emptyset = A$ is like the $a + 0 = a$ property of numbers, $(A')' = A$ reminds one of the $-(-a) = a$ property of numbers, while "If $A' = B'$ then $A = B$," is like "If $1/a = 1/b$ then $a = b$." But numbers do not possess all the properties which parallel those mentioned in our set theorems. For example, $A \cup S = S$ is true of sets according to Theorem 15 but $a + 1 = 1$ is not true of numbers; the idempotency properties of $\cup$ and $\cap$ in Theorem 10 are true of all sets but $x + x = x$ and $x \cdot x = x$ are not true for all numbers. Which of the properties of $\cup$, $\cap$, $\emptyset$ and S in the set theorems parallel properties of $+$, $\cdot$, 0, and 1 in the number system? Using Theorems 1 through 31, list as many properties of the number system as you can.

3-2. For each of the following cases, give an example of a probability domain D which satisfies all four axioms.
   a. D has exactly two members and $S = \{0, 1\}$.
   b. D has exactly four members and $S = \{0, 1, 2\}$.
   c. D has exactly eight members and $S = \{0, 1, 2, 3\}$.
   d. D has exactly sixteen members and $S = \{0, 1, 2, 3, 4\}$.
   e. D has exactly thirty-two members and $S = \{0, 1, 2, 3, 4, 5\}$.
   f. D has *less* than thirty-two members and $S = \{0, 1, 2, 3, 4, 5\}$.
   What do you suspect about the relationship between the number of members of $S - \emptyset$ and the number of members of D, if $S - \emptyset$ is not infinite?

3-3. Give examples of D's satisfying: (a) only Axiom I, (b) only Axiom II, (c) only Axiom III, (d) only Axiom IV, (e) only Axioms I and II, (f) only Axioms I and III, (g) only Axioms I and IV, (h) only Axioms II and III, (i) only Axioms II and IV, and (j) only Axioms III and IV.

3-4. Why does the collection D_1 of all circle-interiors in the plane satisfy only one axiom? Why does the collection D_2 of all interiors of plane circles which are centered at the point $(0, 0)$ and have diameters of at least 3 but not more than 10 satisfy only three of our axioms?

3-5. Show that, if D's only member is S, then D satisfies all four axioms.

3-6. Prove the following theorem without using Theorems 1 to 31.
   Theorem 32. *D covers S. That is, each member of S is also a member of some set in the collection D.*
   Give an example in which D does not cover S, but three of our axioms are satisfied.

3-7. Explain why the collection D of all the point sets in the plane which contain the point $(0, 0)$ as a member satisfies all four axioms. Is the point $(0, 0)$ the same as the *set* $\emptyset$ or only a *member* of $\emptyset$?

3-8. Consider the U. S. electorate example given in Section 3-2 of this chapter. Explain why it satisfies Axiom II but not Axiom III. In order to satisfy Axiom III, let us now suppose that the only person who is a member of more than one party is Rasputin de Spicable, who belongs to all four parties and keeps it under his hat. (Rasputin is not really a political spy; it is just that he is an easy man to convince.) Let D have six members: the U. S. electorate, the Democratic Party, the Republican Party, the Socialist Party, the Prohibition Party, and the set whose only member is Rasputin de Spicable. Why doesn't D satisfy Axiom IV? Define and add the four sets to D which are necessary to satisfy Axiom IV. Why doesn't your resulting D satisfy Axiom II? Add the six sets to D which are necessary to satisfy Axiom II. Show that all four axioms are now satisfied by this sixteen-member collection D. Explain why S and D are different sets. Explain why nothing is a member of both D and S and why no member of D is a person.

3–9. How does $\tilde{X}$ differ from X'? Can it be shown that there is a member of D which is neither S nor $\emptyset$?

3–10. Why is it not possible to have a nondegenerate probability domain D whose number of members is odd?

3–11. Suppose the set A is a member of the probability domain D and that D_1 is the collection such that a thing is a member of D_1 if and only if that thing is the common part of A with some member of D. Show that D_1 is also a probability domain.

3–12. Every line interval is a set of points. Suppose the line intervals A, B, and C form a triangle whose vertices are the points p, q, and r. Which axioms are satisfied by D_1: $\{A, B, C, \{p\}, \{q\}, \{r\}, A \cup B \cup C\}$? Can you add sets to D_1 so that the result satisfies Axioms I, II, and IV only? Axioms I, II, and III only?

3–13. Use Boolean algebra to show each of the following.
     a. $A \cap A' = S'$
     b. $X \cup X' = (Y \cap \emptyset)'$
     c. $A \cup (B \cup A) = A \cup B$
     d. $A \cap (A' \cup B) = A \cap B$
     e. $(B \cap A') \cup A = A \cup B$
     f. $A \cap (A \cup B) = A$ (Try Theorem 5)
     g. $X \cup (Y \cap X) = X$
     h. $(L \cap M) \cup (L \cap M') = L$
     i. $(A \cap B) \cup (A \cap B') \cup (A' \cap B) = A \cup B$
     j. $(X \cup Y) \cap (X \cup Y') \cap (X' \cup Y) \cap (X' \cup Y') = \emptyset$
     k. $(X_1 \cup X_2 \cup X_3 \cup X_4)' = X_1' \cap X_2' \cap X_3' \cap X_4'$ (de Morgan's
     l. $(X_1 \cap X_2 \cap X_3 \cap X_4)' = X_1' \cup X_2' \cup X_3' \cup X_4'$ Laws)
     m. $X \cup (S - Y) = X \cup Y'$

3-14. Prove the following in any way you wish.

Theorem 32. *D covers S.*

Theorem 33. *If A and B are members of D such that $A \cup B = S$ and $A \cap B = \emptyset$, then $B = A'$.*

Theorem 34. *If L and M are sets such that $\emptyset$ does not intersect $L \cap M$, then $L \cap M = [(L \cap M) \cup \emptyset] - \emptyset$.*

Theorem 35. *If A and B are members of D, then $A \cup (S - B) = A \cup B'$ and, if $A \cap (S - B)$ exists, then $A \cap (S - B) = (A \cap B') - \emptyset = S - (A' \cup B) = A - B$.*

3-15. Use Boolean algebra to show each of the following. (See Question 2-8.)

 a. $(\tilde{A} \widetilde{\cup} \tilde{B}) \cup (A \widetilde{\cup} B) = (\tilde{A} \cap \tilde{B}) \cup (B \cap A)$
$= (\tilde{A} \cup B) \cap (\tilde{B} \cup A)$

 b. $A \cap (\tilde{A} \cup B) = A \cap B$

 c. $(A \cap \tilde{B}) \cup (A \cap B) = A$

 d. $\tilde{A} \cup [(A \cup B) \cap (A \cup \tilde{B})] = S$

3-16. Why don't the six sets shown in the right-hand diagram of Figure 2-12a form a probability-partition-with-respect-to-D of the set S? How could you use the six sets in this diagram to define the members of a D which satisfies all four axioms?

3-17. Suppose S is the interior of the circle in Figure 2-11b and $\emptyset$ is the set whose only member is the center-point of the circle. Let the center-point be included in each of the eleven sets shown and let a probability domain D be defined so that all these eleven sets belong to D. Then the right-hand part of Figure 2-11b illustrates a probability-partition-with-respect-to-D of S. Explain why the left-hand part of Figure 2-11b also illustrates a probability-partition-with-respect-to-D of S. What list of sets is a probability-partition-with-respect-to-D of the management set?

3-18. In Figure 3-1, why isn't $\{X, Y\}$ a probability-partition-with-respect-to-D of S? The set $\{X, Y\}$ *is* a probability-partition-with-respect-to-D of what set? In Figure 3-2, why isn't $\{A, B, A' \cap B'\}$ a probability-partition-with-respect-to-D of S?

3-19. Suppose that in the wording of Axiom III we replace $\emptyset$ by $\emptyset_1$, and in the wording of Axiom IV we replace each $\emptyset$ by $\emptyset_2$. Is it possible now to show that $\emptyset_1$ is the same as $\emptyset_2$, or must we add another axiom to get the $\emptyset_1 = \emptyset_2$ result?

3-20. Show that A and B are members of D, then
$$A \cap B \subseteq A \cup B, \qquad A - B \subseteq S - B, \qquad A - B \subseteq A \cap B',$$
$$[\emptyset \cup (S - B \cap S)] \cap B \subseteq (B \cap A) \cup (A \cap B'),$$
$$A' \cap B' \subseteq (A \cap B)'.$$

chapter four

Permutations, Combinations, and Counting of Sets

4–1. BACKGROUND AND REASONS FOR COUNTING THE NUMBER OF MEMBERS OF A SET

The statement that k is a counting number means that k is a number used in counting. That is, k is one of the numbers 1, 2, 3, $\cdots$. *The statement that the set M is countable, or denumerable, means there exists a one-to-one correspondence between the members of M and some subset of the set of all counting numbers.* For example, the English alphabet is countable because there exists a one-to-one correspondence between the twenty-six letters and a subset of the set of counting numbers, namely the first twenty-six counting numbers. The one-to-one correspondence is *A* to 1, *B* to 2, *C* to 3, $\cdots$, *Z* to 26. As a second example, the set of all even numbers is countable: 2 corresponds to 1, 4 to 2, 6 to 3, 8 to 4, 10 to 5, $\cdots$. The subset of all the counting numbers being used in this second example is the set of *all* counting numbers.

66

The statement that the set M is finite means that there is some counting number k such that M has exactly k members. The statement that the set M is infinite means that M is not finite. The alphabet is finite, but the set of all even numbers is infinite. If it were possible for a wrist watch to be *really* self-winding, the set of all its ticks would be countable and infinite. The set of all broken parking meters (at this moment) is, alas, quite finite. The X axis is obviously an infinite point set. (Can you decide whether it is also countable?) We are, as you will see, very much interested in the counting of sets when set theory is applied to probability problems.

In a probability problem we are concerned with some "experiment," or "chance situation," which has more than one "possible outcome." Some of the possible outcomes are "significant outcomes," while the rest are "insignificant outcomes." If, for instance, one toss of two coins is our experiment, then there are only four significant outcomes: both heads, both tails, head and tail, tail and head. But there are many possible outcomes which are insignificant, such as the outcome in which one of the coins comes to rest leaning against a wall or perhaps bounces out a window and is lost. Another example of a possible outcome which is insignificant would be the outcome in the duel example of Chapter 1 in which Caspar Queeze finds a way to fall into a mail box on his way to the duel and never arrives on the field of honor. This is a possible outcome, but we would not want it to affect our computations of probabilities, so we would assign it a probability of zero.

The mathematical model we use for a probability problem is some kind of probability domain D. Each possible outcome of the experiment is represented by a member of S in the model, so that S represents the set of all possible outcomes. (S is often referred to as a "sample space.") We represent the set of all the insignificant outcomes by the set $\emptyset$, and the set of all significant outcomes by the set $S - \emptyset$. For instance, $S - \emptyset$ for the experiment "one flip of two coins" would represent the four–member set of possible outcomes {(heads heads), (tails tails), (heads tails), (tails heads)}. All other possible outcomes, such as losing the coin, are insignificant and are represented in the model as members of $\emptyset$. "Event" is the term applied to each set of possible outcomes which contains all the insignificant outcomes. We let the members of D in our model represent the events in our chance situation, because each member of D contains all the members of $\emptyset$. For instance, the event in which we do not get two tails—represent it by B in the model—would be the set whose members are all the possible outcomes except (tails tails). Note that this event is a subset of the set of all possible outcomes, and this event contains the set of all insignificant outcomes (represented by $\emptyset$ in the model) as a subset. Paralleling this in our model, B is a subset of S, and B contains all members of $\emptyset$. (We want

B to be a member of D, of course.) We see then that "event" in the chance situation is analogous to "member of D" in the model, "insignificant outcome" is analogous to "member of $\emptyset$," and "significant outcome" is like "member of $S - \emptyset$," when a probability domain D is a model for a "chance situation."

Suppose we encounter a chance situation for which $S - \emptyset$ is finite. Then if X represents an event, the set $X - \emptyset$ is also finite, and we will want the "probability of the event X" to mean the number of significant outcomes which are members of X divided by the total number of significant outcomes which are possible for this experiment. Thus, *if D is a probability domain such that $S - \emptyset$ is finite and if X is a member of D, then let* No. (X) *denote the number of members of $X - \emptyset$. Moreover, let* No. $(\emptyset)$ *mean zero.* For instance, in the coin-flipping experiment above, No. (B) is 3 and No. (S) is 4. Then the probability of the event B, in which the significant outcomes are those in which at least one coin shows heads, would be No. $(B)/$No. (S), which is 3/4. The probability of the event $\emptyset$, in which no significant outcome occurs, would be No. $(\emptyset)/$No. (S), which is 0/4, which is zero. The probability that something significant occurs would be No. $(S)/$No. (S), which is 4/4, or one.

Be sure to observe that No. has the following properties. If D is a probability domain such that $S - \emptyset$ is finite, then No. is defined for all members of D. No. (S) is greater than zero (how do we know this?) and No. $(\emptyset) = 0$. If X is a member of D, then $0 \leq$ No. $(X) \leq$ No. (S). Lastly, if X and Y are members of D, then No. $(X \cup Y) =$ No. $(X) +$ No. (Y) $-$ No. $(X \cap Y)$; this is referred to as the *additive* property. Mathematicians speak of No. as a "set-function" whose "domain" is D, and they are likely to use the symbol $N(X)$ or $n(X)$ instead of our No.(X).

From No.$(X \cup Y) =$ No.$(X) +$ No.$(Y) -$ No.$(X \cap Y)$, the additive property, it can be shown that

$$\begin{aligned}
\text{No.}(W \cup X \cup Y) = {} & \text{No.}(W) + \text{No.}(X) + \text{No.}(Y) \\
& - \text{No.}(W \cap X) - \text{No.}(W \cap Y) \\
& - \text{No.}(X \cap Y) + \text{No.}(W \cap X \cap Y)
\end{aligned}$$

and

$$\begin{aligned}
\text{No.}(V \cup W \cup X \cup Y) = {} & \text{No.}(V) + \text{No.}(W) + \text{No.}(X) \\
& + \text{No.}(Y) - \text{No.}(V \cap W) \\
& - \text{No.}(V \cap X) - \text{No.}(V \cap Y) \\
& - \text{No.}(W \cap X) - \text{No.}(W \cap Y) \\
& - \text{No.}(X \cap Y) + \text{No.}(V \cap W \cap X) \\
& + \text{No.}(V \cap W \cap Y) + \text{No.}(V \cap X \cap Y) \\
& + \text{No.}(W \cap X \cap Y) \\
& - \text{No.}(V \cap W \cap X \cap Y),
\end{aligned}$$

in which all sets are members of the same probability domain D. All three equations are special cases of the so-called *in-and-out-theorem* of probability theory. Questions 2–16 and 2–17 illustrate the first and third of these equations, respectively, while the second equation above is illustrated by Question 2–15 and by the green-rubber-cube example in Section 2–7 of Chapter 2.

We shall concern ourselves with only those probability domains D for which $S - \emptyset$ is finite and for which D is, therefore, also finite. A more advanced treatment which includes infinite probability domains D would require the addition of a fifth axiom which would insure that every infinite collection of members of D would have a common part which is also a member of D. But we shall consider only D's which are finite.

4–2. PERMUTATIONS

The fundamental principle for the counting of significant outcomes in an event which is composed of two events is as follows.

Theorem 36. If an event X can happen in exactly No.(X) *ways* (significant outcomes of an experiment E_1) *and if an event Y can happen in exactly* No.(Y) *ways* (significant outcomes of another experiment E_2), *then $X \cap Y$* (the event that both of the events X and Y occur when both experiments E_1 and E_2 are performed) *can occur in exactly* No.$(X) \cdot$ No.(Y) *ways* (significant outcomes of the compound experiment $E_1 - E_2$).*

For example, an even number can occur as the score on one flip of a die in three ways, while an ace can be selected in one draw from a deck of playing cards in four ways. Hence, the event in which an even score and an ace are both obtained can occur in three times four, or twelve ways.

Suppose we have an urn containing fifteen pool balls numbered from 1 to 15. Obviously, the event in which we draw a ball from the urn can occur in fifteen ways. If we draw a ball, note its number, replace it in the urn, and then draw again (possibly obtaining the same ball), noting the num-

---

*Each significant outcome in the event $X \cap Y$ of the compound experiment $E_1 - E_2$ is a *pair* of significant outcomes, one from the event X of experiment E_1 and the other from the event Y of experiment E_2. Hence, $(X \cap Y) - \emptyset$ is a set of pairs. Now, if we adopt the convention that in each pair the significant outcome from E_1 is always listed first and the significant outcome from E_2 is always listed second, the result is a set of *ordered* pairs. When the *set* $(X \cap Y) - \emptyset$ of all significant outcomes in $X \cap Y$ is listed as the above set of ordered pairs, then $(X \cap Y) - \emptyset$ is called the *Cartesian product* of the sets $X - \emptyset_{E_1}$ and $Y - \emptyset_{E_2}$. The symbol $A \times B$ is often used to denote the Cartesian product of a set A and a set B, if members of A precede members of B in the ordering of pairs.

ber, there are 15 times 15, or 225 possible results. If there had been n balls numbered from 1 to n in the urn, then there would have been n ways to draw one ball and n times n, or n^2, ways to draw two balls—with replacement. If the first ball is not replaced before the second draw, then there is one less ball which may be drawn on the second draw. This would be referred to as drawing *without replacement* or *without repetition*. In the case of the fifteen-ball urn there are 15 times 14, or 210 ways to draw two balls without replacement; but in the case of the n-ball urn there are n times $n - 1$, or $n(n - 1)$ ways to draw twice without repetition. Figure 4–1 uses a tree diagram to illustrate this principle for the case of a four-ball urn.

If we draw three times without replacement from the fifteen-ball urn there are fifteen ways of selecting the first ball, and for each of these ways there are only fourteen ways of drawing the second time. For each of these 15×14 ways in which the first two draws can be made without replacement, there are only thirteen balls left for the third draw; hence there are a total of $15 \times 14 \times 13$ ways we can draw three times without repetition. If, on the other hand, we replace each ball in the urn before drawing again, there are $15 \times 15 \times 15$ or $(15)^3$ ways of drawing three balls with repetition from the fifteen-ball urn. In the case of the n-ball urn, there are $n(n - 1)(n - 2)$ ways of drawing three times without replacement and n^3 ways of drawing three times with replacement. This could be illustrated with

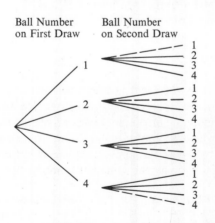

Ball Number
on First Draw

Ball Number
on Second Draw

Dotted-line possibilities are included only in the case where repetition is possible. There are
a. 4×4, or 16 possibilities if repetition is allowed, and
b. 4×3, or 12 possibilities if repetition is not allowed.

FIGURE 4–1. A Tree Diagram Illustrating the Number of Possible Ways We Can Draw Twice (a) with Replacement and (b) without Replacement from an Urn Containing 4 Balls Numbered from 1 to 4

Ball Number on   Ball Number on   Ball Number on
First Draw   Second Draw   Third Draw

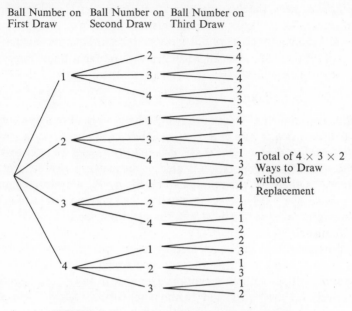

Total of 4 × 3 × 2
Ways to Draw
without
Replacement

FIGURE 4–2. A Tree Diagram Illustrating the
Number of Possible Ways 3 Balls
Can Be Drawn without Repetition
from an Urn Containing 4 Numbered Balls

tree diagrams. If we do not allow repetition, the tree would have n large
branches, each sprouting $n-1$ small branches, with each of these
small branches sprouting $n-2$ twigs. Figure 4–2 shows this for the case
where $n = 4$. There would be $n(n-1)(n-2)$ twigs, one for each way
we can draw three balls from the n-ball urn without repetition. If we allow
repetition, the tree would have more branches and twigs.

To extend this reasoning, if we draw r times from the fifteen-ball
urn, there are 15^r ways this can be done with repetition and there are
$(15)(14)(13) \cdots (15 - r + 1)$ ways this can be done without repetition if
r does not exceed 15. If, on the other hand, we draw r times from
the n-ball urn, there are n^r ways this can occur with repetition and
$n(n-1)(n-2) \cdots (n - r + 1)$ ways it can occur without repetition.
When repetition is not allowed, r obviously cannot exceed n. If we draw
n times from the n-ball urn, then there are n^n ways of drawing with repetition and $n(n-1)(n-2) \cdots (3)(2)(1)$ ways of drawing without repetition.

In order to simplify the notation, let us make some definitions. *If and
only if k is a counting number greater than 1, let k! denote the product of k*

and all the counting numbers less than k; moreover, let $1! = 1$ *and* $0! = 1$. For instance, $7! = (7)(6) \cdots (2)(1)$, which is 5,040. We refer to $k!$ as "k factorial." (Sometimes the symbol $\lfloor k$ is used for $k!$.) Then there are $n!$ ways we can draw all n balls from an n-ball urn without repetition. Observe that $n! = [n(n-1)(n-2) \cdots (n-r+1)] \cdot (n-r)!$, so that

$$n(n-1)(n-2) \cdots (n-r+1) = n!/(n-r)!,$$

which is the number of ways of drawing r balls without replacement from an n-ball urn. *If h is zero or a counting number and k is a counting number which is not less than h, then let* $k^{(h)}$ *denote* $k!/(k-h)!$; we refer to $k^{(h)}$ as "k upper h." (This $k^{(h)}$ notation is used in the mathematical field of finite differences. Otherwise, the notations $P(k, h)$, or ${}^kP_h$, are more commonly used instead of $k^{(h)}$.) Now we can say that the number of ways of drawing r times from an n-ball urn is n^r if with repetition, and is $n^{(r)}$ if without repetition and $r \leq n$.

Future confusion can be avoided by regarding each way of selecting r times from n items as an r-term sequence which is "made from" the n items either with or without repetition. There are n^r and $n^{(r)}$ such sequences respectively for the "with" and "without repetition" cases. For example, each result of selecting six balls with repetition from an urn containing fifteen pool balls (numbered from 1 to 15) can be regarded as a six-term sequence made from the first fifteen counting numbers with repetition. There are 15^6 such sequences. The number of arrangements of the seven letters in the word "confuse" is the same as the number of seven-term sequences which can be made from the first seven counting numbers without repetition. There are $7^{(7)}$ such sequences. Observe that $7^{(7)} = 7!/(7-7)!$, which is $7!/0!$, or $7!/1$, or just $7!$.

We shall take *sequence* and *term* and *order* as undefined notions here. Two differences between the notion of *sequence* and the notion of *set* are that (1) the terms of a sequence are ordered, but the members of a set carry no notion of ordering; and (2) it is possible for two terms of a sequence to be the same thing, but we do not allow two members of a set to be the same thing. The terms of each sequence are ordered because we can talk about the "first term" of a sequence or the "eighth term" of a sequence, but there is no "first member" of a set because *set* does not imply an ordering of the membership. It is possible for two terms of a sequence to be the same thing, as, for example, in the number sequence 3, 5, 2, 5, 0, 5, 7, 3, 8, which has been made from the number set {3, 5, 2, 0, 7, 8}. But no repetition of membership in a set is allowed by our notion of *set*. *The statement that the number sequence* $a_1, a_2, a_3, \ldots, a_k$ *is an increasing sequence means that* $a_1 < a_2 < a_3 < \ldots < a_k$. *The statement that the number sequence* $a_1, a_2, a_3, \ldots, a_k$ *is nondecreasing means that* $a_1 \leq a_2 \leq a_3$

$\leqq \ldots \leqq a_k$. For example, -5, -2, 0, 3, 4, $4\frac{1}{2}$, 7, 8 is increasing, but 2, 5, 4, $4\frac{1}{2}$, 7, 3 and 2, 3, 3, 7, 8, 8 are not. The sequences 1, 2, 3, 4, 5, 6 and 1, 2, 2, 4, 4, 4, 4, 5 are nondecreasing, but 1, 2, 3, 2, 4 is not nondecreasing. Obviously, repetition of terms is possible in a nondecreasing number-sequence but not in an increasing number-sequence.

Theorem 37. *If n is a counting number and r is a counting number and M is an n-member set then there are n^r r-term sequences which can be made from the members of M with repetition.*

Theorem 38. *If n is a counting number and r is a counting number which is not greater than n and M is an n-member set, then there are $n^{(r)}$, or $n!/(n-r)!$, r-term sequences which can be made from the members of M without repetition.*

If n is a counting number and M is an n-member set, then List L (call it that) is said to be an *r-term permutation of the set M*, or a *permutation of the members of M taken r at a time*, if and only if r is a counting number not greater than n and List L is an r-term sequence made from the members of M without repetition. Hence, *permutation* merely means "sequence made without repetition." The sequence of letters Y, A, K, F, U, Z, for instance, is a six-term permutation of the letters of the alphabet, or a permutation of the twenty-six letters of the alphabet taken six at a time. The sequence Z, U, K, F, A, Y is another one, and so is A, B, C, D, E, F. In practice, the number of n-term permutations of an n-member set is referred to merely as the number of *permutations* of the set, and this is $n!$, as we have seen.

It is instructive to consider some situations in which we desire to know how many permutations or sequences of a certain kind are possible. How many auto license plates consisting of six-place numbers are possible if each place may contain one of the ten digits 1, 2, 3, $\ldots$, 9, 0? The answer is 10^6, the number of six-term sequences which can be made with repetition from the first ten counting numbers. How many seven-place auto license plates consisting of three letters and four digits are possible if both letters and digits can repeat? This would be $26^3 \cdot 10^4$, because there are 26^3 possible three-term sequences with repetition from the twenty-six letters, and for each of these sequences there are 10^4 possible four-term sequences from the ten digits with repetition. If we modify this problem so that the letters cannot repeat but the digits can, the answer is $26^{(3)} \cdot 10^4$, which is $(26!/23!) \cdot 10^4$.

The number of six-letter words which are possible if no letter appears twice in the same word is $26^{(6)}$, or $26!/(26-6)!$, which is the same as the number of six-term sequences which can be made from the first twenty-six counting numbers without repetition. There are $26!$ twenty-six–term permutations of the letters of the alphabet. (Note that $26^{(26)} = 26!$.)

There are $6^{(5)}$ ways in which five people can occupy six stools at a soda fountain. This is without repetition because no stool can be used by two or more people. There are 6^5 results possible on one toss of five dice. This is with repetition because two dice can show the same score. If ten coins are tossed, there are 2^{10} possible results: the number of ten-term sequences which can be made from the two members of the set {heads, tails} with repetition.

Theorem 39. *Of each n-member set, there exist $2^n - 1$ subsets. Moreover, if each subset of S which contains all members of $\emptyset$ is a member of the probability domain D, and if $S - \emptyset$ is finite, then D has exactly $2^{\text{No.}(S)}$ members.*

You should be able to prove this one easily now.

There are $n!$ ways in which n people can enter a room. In how many ways can three men seat themselves at six counter stools if no two men are on adjacent stools? The stools can be occupied in the four possible patterns XOXOXO, XOXOOX, XOOXOX, or OXOXOX, and for each of these occupancy patterns the three men can seat themselves in the three occupied stools in 3! ways. Hence, $4 \cdot 3!$ is the answer.

The following example is more complicated. In how many orders can a deck of playing cards be dealt to four bridge players so that Mr. North receives at least two aces, and he receives all his aces before he receives any lower-valued cards? To solve this, we can split it into three mutually exclusive cases: (1) North gets exactly two aces, (2) North gets exactly three aces, and (3) North gets all four aces. In case (1) there are $4^{(2)}$ orders in which he can be dealt two aces of the four, and for each of these orders the other two aces can appear in the thirty-nine cards of the other three players in $39^{(2)} \cdot 2!$ ways. Then in case (1) all four aces can be dealt out in $4^{(2)} \cdot 39^{(2)} \cdot 2!$ ways, and for each of these, the forty-eight "hand-offs" in which aces are not dealt may be occupied in 48! possible orders by the other forty-eight cards. Hence, case (1) can occur in exactly $4^{(2)} \cdot 39^{(2)} \cdot 2! \cdot 48!$ ways. Similarly, cases (2) and (3) can occur in $4^{(3)} \cdot 39^{(1)} \cdot 1! \cdot 48!$ and $4^{(4)} \cdot 39^{(0)} \cdot 0! \cdot 48!$ ways, respectively. The total number of dealing orders for all three cases is $4^{(2)} \cdot 39^{(2)} \cdot 2! \cdot 48! + 4^{(3)} \cdot 39^{(1)} \cdot 1! \cdot 48! + 4^{(4)} \cdot 39^{(0)} \cdot 0! \cdot 48!$, which simplifies to our answer: $(4!39!48!)/(37!) + 4!(39)48! + 4!48!$.

We have seen that $n!$ is the number of n-term sequences which can be made from a set of n things without repetition. But how many of these sequences would we human beings be able to distinguish if some of the n things look alike to us? Suppose, for instance, that we have fifteen pool balls, of which eleven are numbered from 1 to 11 and the other four are cue balls which all look alike? To answer this, we reason as follows. There must exist some counting number which is the number of fifteen-term sequences which can be made from these balls without repetition and such that we could *distinguish* between them. Let a denote this counting number. Certainly a is less than 15! because, for each sequence we can distinguish, there are 4! ways the four cue balls could have been placed in their four positions. Then a times 4! accounts for all 15! permutations of the fifteen balls. That is, $a \cdot (4!) = 15!$, and the equation $a = 15!/4!$ gives us the number of distinguishable sequences.

We can now answer the question, "How many different permutations are there of all the letters in the word 'passions'?" There will be fewer than 8! permutations because the three letters s are alike. Using reasoning like that in the preceding paragraph, we find that $8!/3!$ is the answer.

But what if there are two or more subsets of look-alikes (the members of each such subset being unlike the members of the other subsets of look-alikes, of course)? Suppose, for instance, that we have fifteen pool balls, of which six are numbered from 1 to 6 and four are alike cue balls and five are alike eight-balls. How many fifteen-term sequences without repetition can be made from them which we can *distinguish*? To answer this, we take the last reasoning process one step further. Let b denote this number of sequences which are distinguishable. Certainly b is less than a (the number a in the preceding pool-ball example) because for each distinguishable sequence in which the five eight-balls are alike and the four cue balls are alike, there are exactly 5! of the a distinguishable sequences in which only the four cue balls are alike and the other eleven balls are unlike. The 5! is due to the fact that the five eight-ball positions can be filled in with five eight-balls in 5! ways. Hence b times 5! accounts for all a of the sequences in which only the four cue balls are look-alikes. That is, $b \cdot (5!) = a$, and a is $15!/4!$. Then b must be $15!/(5!4!)$, and this is our answer. A further extension of this reasoning process would show that the number of distinguishable permutations of fifteen pool balls, of which four are numbered from 1 to 4, two are alike seven-balls, five are alike eight-balls, and four are alike cue balls, is the number $15!/(2!5!4!)$.

Theorem 40. Suppose M is an n-member set. Suppose also that M_1 is an n_1-member subset of alike members of M and M_2 is an n_2-member subset of alike members of M ... and M_k is an n_k-member subset of alike members of M, and no member of one of the sets $M_1, M_2, \ldots, M_k$ is like some member of another of the sets $M_1, M_2, \ldots, M_k$, and each member (if any) of $M - (M_1 \cup M_2 \cup \cdots \cup M_k)$ is unique in appearance. Then $n!/(n_1!n_2! \cdots n_k!)$ is the number of distinguishable permutations of M.

To illustrate with other examples, there are $13!/(3!2!4!)$ different arrangements of the thirteen letters in the word "simplicissmus" because the letter i appears three times, the letter m appears twice and the letter s appears four times. There are $15!/(3!4!2!6!)$ permutations of the sequence 1, 1, 1, 2, 2, 2, 2, 3, 3, 4, 4, 4, 4, 4, 4, while there are $4!/(2!2!)$ permutations of the letters in the word "deed," and $7!/(2!2!)$ in "deeding."

4-3. COMBINATIONS AND THE BINOMIAL THEOREM

Suppose there are eight pool balls, numbered from 1 to 8, in an eight-position rack composed of eight boxes in a row, each box having room enough for only one ball. As we have seen, the balls must lie in one of 8! possible sequences, because repetition is not possible. Now consider the one-ball, two-ball, and three-ball: they occupy a set of three boxes. How many possible three-box sets are there for these three balls to occupy? (The wording of this last sentence implies that, for each three-box set, we are unconcerned about which of the three boxes contains the one-ball, which contains the two-ball, and which contains the three-ball. We do care about which three boxes are occupied, but not how the one-, two-, and three-balls are distributed to them.) This question is equivalent to the question, "How many three-member subsets are there of an eight-member set?" Notice that this would be the same as the number of five-member subsets of an eight-member set, because to choose a subset of three is the same as selecting a subset of five "unchosen" members. In general, the number of r-member subsets of an n-member set is the same as the number of $(n - r)$-member subsets of the n-member set.

To answer the question for our pool-ball example, let c denote the number of three-box sets which can be occupied by the three balls. Each of these c sets can be pictured as one of the following occupancy patterns.

XXXOOOOO XXOXOOOO ··· XXOOOOOX
XOXXOOOO XOXOXOOO ··· OOOOOXXX

The total number of patterns is c, of course, and we can determine what number c is by relating it to 8!, the total number of permutations of all eight balls, in the following manner. The first of the c patterns applies to how many of the 8! permutations? The three "X boxes" can be filled with the one-, two-, and three-balls in 3! ways, and for each of these the five "O boxes" can be filled with the other five balls in 5! ways. Hence 3! times 5! of those 8! permutations are associated with the first occupancy pattern, XXXOOOOO. But by the same reasoning we can show, for *each* pattern, that it is associated with 3!5! of those 8! permutations. Since there are c patterns, then c times $3!5!$ accounts for all $8!$ permutations of the eight balls. Hence, $c \cdot (3!5!) = 8!$, and the equation $c = 8!/(3!5!)$ gives us the number of three-member subsets (also the number of five-member subsets) which can be selected from an eight-member set.

Pause now and show that there are $12!/3!5!4!$ ways in which a twelve-member set can be partitioned into three subsets of three members, five members, and four members.

Now that you have shown this, observe how much labor you could have saved by using Theorem 40. Both the preceding problems are special cases of Theorem 40, because the X's are indistinguishable and the O's are indistinguishable.

In the literature the symbol $\left(\begin{smallmatrix} & n & \\ r_1 & r_2 \cdots & r_k \end{smallmatrix}\right)$ is often used to denote $\dfrac{n!}{(r_1!)(r_2!)\cdots(r_k!)}$ when n is a nonnegative integer and $r_1 + r_2 + \cdots + r_k = n$. The number $12!/(3!5!4!)$ would be denoted $\left(\begin{smallmatrix} & 12 & \\ 3 & 5 & 4 \end{smallmatrix}\right)$. The number $8!/(3!5!)$ can be denoted $\left(\begin{smallmatrix} & 8 & \\ 3 & 5 \end{smallmatrix}\right)$, but since the 8 and the 3 determine that the other number in the parentheses must be 5 (the top number 8 must be the sum of the bottom numbers 3 and 5) this is usually shortened to just $\left(\begin{smallmatrix} 8 \\ 3 \end{smallmatrix}\right)$. The symbols $\left(\begin{smallmatrix} n \\ r \end{smallmatrix}\right)$ or $\left(\begin{smallmatrix} & n & \\ n & - & r \end{smallmatrix}\right)$ are customarily used in place of $\left(\begin{smallmatrix} & n & \\ r & n & - & r \end{smallmatrix}\right)$. Other symbols often used for $n!/r!(n-r)!$ are ^nC_r, C_r^n, $_nC_r$, and $C(n, r)$.

It is well to observe that, if n is a nonnegative integer, then $\left(\begin{smallmatrix} n \\ 0 \end{smallmatrix}\right)$ and $\left(\begin{smallmatrix} n \\ n \end{smallmatrix}\right)$ are each equal to 1, while $\left(\begin{smallmatrix} n \\ 1 \end{smallmatrix}\right)$ and $\left(\begin{smallmatrix} & n & \\ n & - & 1 \end{smallmatrix}\right)$ are each equal to n. Moreover, $\left(\begin{smallmatrix} n \\ r \end{smallmatrix}\right)$ is the coefficient of the $r + 1$ term in the "binomial expansion" of $(A + B)^n$, according to the binomial theorem.

Theorem 41. *If x is a number* (any number: positive or negative, rational or irrational) *and A is a number and B is a number, and* 0^0 *means* 1 (in this theorem only), *then*

$$(A + B)^x = A^x + \frac{x}{1} A^{x-1}B + \frac{x(x-1)}{1 \cdot 2} A^{x-2}B^2$$
$$+ \frac{x(x-1)(x-2)}{1 \cdot 2 \cdot 3} A^{x-3}B^3 + \cdots,$$

where $-1 < B/A < 1$ *if x is not zero or a counting number.*

When x is a counting number, say n, all terms after the $n + 1$ term have coefficients of zero (see Theorem 52, part 1) and we have

$$(A + B)^n = 1 \cdot A^n B^0 + \frac{n}{1} A^{n-1} B^1 + \frac{n(n-1)}{1 \cdot 2} A^{n-2} B^2$$

$$+ \frac{n(n-1)(n-2)}{1 \cdot 2 \cdot 3} A^{n-3} B^3 + \cdots + \frac{n(n-1) \cdots (n-r+1)}{1 \cdot 2 \cdots r} A^{n-r} B^r$$

$$+ \cdots + \frac{n(n-1) \cdots 2 \cdot 1}{1 \cdot 2 \cdots (n-1)n} A^{n-n} B^n.$$

But the coefficients can be written so that

$$(A + B)^n = \binom{n}{0} A^n B^0 + \binom{n}{1} A^{n-1} B^1 + \binom{n}{2} A^{n-2} B^2 + \cdots$$

$$+ \binom{n}{r} A^{n-r} B^r + \cdots + \binom{n}{n} A^{n-n} B^n,$$

and we see that $\binom{n}{r}$ is the coefficient of the $r + 1$ term. Therefore, a number which is expressed in the form $\binom{x}{r}$ is often called a *binomial coefficient* when r is an integer.

Now let us return to the eight-position-rack example. Instead of using three X's and five O's to represent each of the c occupancy patterns, we could have numbered the boxes from 1 to 8 and then shown, for each of the c patterns, the numbers of the *boxes* occupied by the one-, two-, and three-balls. Thus, XXXOOOOO would be shown as 123, and XXOXOOOO would be 124, and $\cdots$ and OOOOOXXX would be 678. Observe the interesting fact that each is a three-term increasing sequence made from the first eight counting numbers.

Theorem 42. If M is an n-member set and r is a counting number which is not greater than n, then the number of r-member subsets of M is $\binom{n}{r}$, and this is the same as the number of r-term increasing sequences which can be made from the first n counting numbers.

Theorem 43. If M is an n-member set and the sum of the counting numbers $r_1, r_2, \cdots, r_k$ is n, then the number of ways M can be partitioned into k subsets of r_1 members, r_2 members, $\cdots$, and r_k members is $\binom{n}{r_1 \, r_2 \cdots r_k}$.

These subsets we have been considering are referred to as combinations. *The statement that x is a combination of n things, taken r at a time, means that x is an r-member subset of an n-member set.*

Some examples will illustrate how the notion of *combination* and Theorems 42 and 43 are used. Suppose the S.H.R. (Sons of the Haymarket Riot) admire Teddy Roosevelt immensely and plan to erect in his honor a two-million dollar bronze moose (shown in the act of charging up San

Juan Hill) at each of three worthy and deserving town halls. The Sons are presently engaged in selecting the three winners from a roster of twenty eager towns. How many selection results are possible? The answer is the number of three-member subsets which can be selected from a twenty-member set. This number is $\binom{20}{3}$, which can also be called the number of *combinations* of twenty towns taken three at a time.

Suppose the makers of a certain breakfast cereal insert a small prize into each package. Into the last 100 boxes were inserted twenty alike plastic finger rings, thirty alike whistles, thirty-five alike marbles, and fifteen alike autographed pictures of Calvin Coolidge. In how many distinguishable ways can the four *kinds* of prizes be distributed among the 100 purchasers if we ignore the order in which they purchase the boxes? The answer is the number of ways we can partition the set of 100 buyers into four subsets of twenty, thirty, thirty-five and fifteen members. This is $\binom{100}{20\ 30\ 35\ 15}$.

In *each* of the fourteen precincts of a certain city an advertising company plans to place four billboard ads for its leading client. How many ad designs are necessary if no design is to appear twice in a precinct and no two precincts may have the same set of four designs? To answer this we let n denote the minimum number of designs required. The billboards in each precinct form a four-member subset of the n-member set of designs. We require at least fourteen such subsets. That is, n must be such that $\binom{n}{4} \geq 14$. Since $\binom{4}{4} = 1$ and $\binom{5}{4} = 5$ and $\binom{6}{4} = 15$, at least six ad designs are necessary.

Questions

4–1. Show that the set of all proper fractions which have counting-number numerators and counting-number denominators is a countable set.

4–2. Drawing two balls without repetition from an urn containing four pool balls numbered from 1 to 4 is an example of a "chance situation" or "experiment." List all the "significant outcomes." Give two examples of "insignificant outcomes." What are the "possible outcomes"? What do you want "event" to mean? List three events. The sets S, $\emptyset$, $S - \emptyset$, and D in the model represent what in the material-world chance situation? What number is No.(S)? What number is the probability of the event that neither ball drawn is the four-ball?

4-3. In Question 4–2, if W denotes the event in which the first ball drawn is not even-numbered, X denotes the event in which the second ball drawn is not odd-numbered, and Y denotes the event in which the sum of the numbers on the two drawn balls is not greater than three, use the in-and-out-theorem to find the numbers No.$(W \cup X)$ and No.$(W \cup X \cup Y)$.

4-4. In the Professor Chalkstorm Q. van Whitesleeves' example in Section 2–7 of Chapter 2, find No.$(A \cup B \cup C)$ by using the in-and-out-theorem.

4-5. Apply the in-and-out-theorem to Question 2–17 to find the number of employees who are male or college-educated or office workers or under forty years old.

4-6. If D is a probability domain such that $S - \emptyset$ is finite and if $P(X)$ means No.$(X)/$No.(S), show that
a. P is defined for all members of D,
b. $P(\emptyset) = 0$ and $P(S) = 1$,
c. $0 \leq P(X) \leq 1$,
d. P is additive (i.e., $P(X \cup Y) = P(X) + P(Y) - P(X \cap Y)$).

4-7. Using only properties a. through d. in Question 4–6 (i.e., without referring to No.), show that $P(X \cap Y) \leq P(X) \leq P(X \cup Y)$.

4-8. If, in the three in-and-out-theorem equations given in Section 4–1 of Chapter 4, each $\cap$ is changed to $\cup$ and each $\cup$ is changed to $\cap$, which of the three results would be true?

4-9. Four smokers are standing in line to use a cigarette machine which vends seven brands of cigarettes: Fumarillos, Imbecillos, Armadillos, El Manillos, Caparillos, Pussywillows, and Mustard Gassers. In how many ways can they make their selections? What is the answer if no two smokers like the same brand?

4-10. A state's auto license plates consist of three letters followed by four digits. How many plates are possible if repetition (1) is allowed, (2) is not allowed, (3) is allowed only on the digits?

4-11. How many different dinners consisting of a salad, a steak, three vegetables, and a dessert can a diner order at Bucky's Cafe de la Cuisine Magnifique if the à la carte menu lists five kinds of salad, seven kinds of steak, six vegetables, and ten kinds of dessert?

4-12. A factory has ten lathes, four milling machines, three drill presses, and two heat-treatment furnaces, no two of which were purchased at the same time. If the manufacturing sequence for a piece is lathe to milling machine to drill press to lathe to furnace, what is the probability that at all stages in its processing a piece will have been processed by the newest possible equipment?

4–13. In how many ways can eighty cents change be given from three quarters and twelve nickels, if no two of the fifteen coins have the same date? How many first-string teams can a baseball manager select from five pitchers, two catchers, seven infielders, and five outfielders?

4–14. How many five-letter English words are possible (1) if no repetition of letters is allowed and (2) if repetition is allowed? (Assume every five-letter sequence is a word.) In how many sequences can a pool shark sink all fifteen pool balls? How many social security numbers are possible?

4–15. In how many distinguishable ways can we permute the six letters in the word "deeded"? How about "sesame seed"? How about "Ken Sneaksnake"? How about "rubber baby buggy bumpers"?

4–16. Thirteen smokers are standing in line to use the machine in Question 4–9. In how many ways can they select (1) if Armadillos are so popular that they are selected seven times and each of the other brands is selected once, and (2) if Armadillos are selected three times and Pussywillows are selected five times and each of the other brands is selected once?

4–17. A pool-ball rack has room for exactly eight balls, arranged in a row. In how many distinguishable ways can it be completely filled from left to right from a set of (1) the fifteen numbered pool balls and four alike cue balls, (2) the lowest ten numbered balls, five alike eleven-balls, and four alike cue balls, (3) the lowest seven numbered balls, three alike eight-balls, five alike eleven-balls, and four alike cue balls? (This one should separate the reasoners from the memorizers.)

4–18. The makers of Snaggle Toothpaste, the only one which contains Botulism-B, are losing customers rapidly, and they suspect that the name "Snaggle" may lack appeal. How many other seven-letter names, however meaningless, can be made if no name may use a letter more than four times?

4–19. In the card-dealing example which follows Theorem 39 why isn't $\binom{4}{2} \cdot 50!$ the answer?

4–20. For thirteen weeks the makers of a certain breakfast cereal are including in each package a slip with some counting number from 1 to 100,000 printed on it. A customer who gets two slips with the same number wins a prize. If a certain customer buys only one package per week, in how many ways can he win a prize if no one may win two prizes?

4–21. In how many ways can seven men be simultaneously seated at a counter with twelve empty stools (1) if both end stools are occupied by them, (2) if they do not sit down simultaneously, (3) if the remaining five stools are occupied simultaneously by women, (4) if each man sits next to a woman and all sit down simultaneously?

4–22. How many legitimate endings are possible in a game of tic-tac-toe?

4–23. Find the value of each:

$$9^{(3)}, \ 7^{(7)}, \ 6^{(3)}/5^{(4)}, \ \binom{6}{2}, \ \binom{12}{4} \cdot 7^{(4)}, \ \binom{7}{1},$$

$$\binom{7}{6}, \ \binom{7}{0}, \ \binom{13}{4}\binom{9}{5}, \ \binom{0}{0}, \ \binom{7}{3 \ 2 \ 2}, \ \binom{10}{5 \ 0 \ 1 \ 4}.$$

4–24. Explain why the number of distinguishable nine-term permutations of a set of three alike eight-balls and six alike cue balls is the same as the number of possible six-member subsets of a nine-member set. What is the total number of subsets of a nine-member set?

4–25. Why isn't the number of nondecreasing six-term sequences from the first ten counting numbers plus the number of decreasing six-term sequences from the first ten counting numbers the same as the number of six-term sequences from the first ten counting numbers, with repetition?

4–26. In how many ways can we see only ten of the fifteen numbered balls resting on a pool table (in no significant order)? Customarily, seven of the numbered balls are striped and the other eight are solid-colored; in how many ways can we select three striped balls and six solids if selection order is ignored?

4–27. Three of the twelve numbers on a clock face are the vertices of a triangle. Now many such triangles are possible?

4–28. A traveling ballet company gives exactly three ballets per performance. It gives thirty performances, no two of which have the same three ballets. What is the minimum number of ballets in its repertoire?

4–29. In how many sequences can 100 draftees leave a bus and enter an army induction center? If there are only four types of blood—A, B, AB, and O—in how many ways can the line which forms be blood-typed? If, in addition to blood type, they are also classified according to the two kinds of Rh factor—positive or negative—in how many ways can the line which formed receive blood classifications? In how many ways can there be exactly five men in the line who faint at the sight of their own blood? In how many ways can there be at least one man in line who faints when given the dull-needled inoculation for Southeast-Asian Sparlemageetis?

4-30. The fifty-six voters in the little town of One Horse cast twenty-five Republican, twenty-six Democratic, and five Socialist votes in the last presidential election. In how many ways could the fifty-six voters have selected their parties?

4-31. Four boys divide thirty unlike marbles among themselves so that each boy gets exactly half as many marbles as the next oldest boy (if there is a next oldest boy). In how many ways can the boys receive their marbles, if order of receipt is ignored?

4-32. All forty members of a mathematics department are assistant professors. In how many ways can we simultaneously promote ten of these worthy fellows to professor and another fourteen of them to associate professor? After promotions, in how many ways can we simultaneously select two professors, three associate professors, and four assistant professors for the budget committee? If we also simultaneously select three professors, five associate professors, and seven assistant professors for the fussbudget committee, in how many ways can the two committees be selected if the two committees are (1) mutually exclusive and (2) not mutually exclusive?

4-33. Each of the eight football teams in the Southwest Conference is playing another Southwest Conference team this Saturday. In how many ways can the teams be matched?

4-34. If A is an m-member set, then there are only $2^m - 1$ subsets of A. If B is an n-member set then the number of subsets of $A \cup B$ may be counted as follows. There are $2^m - 1$ subsets of $A \cup B$ which contain no members of B; there are $(2^m - 1) \cdot n$ subsets of $A \cup B$ which contain only one member of B; there are $(2^m - 1) \cdot \binom{n}{2}$ subsets of $A \cup B$ which contain only two members of B; $\cdots$; there are $(2^m - 1) \cdot \binom{n}{n}$ subsets of $A \cup B$ which contain all n members of B. Now $(2^m - 1) + (2^m - 1) \cdot n + (2^m - 1) \cdot \binom{n}{2} + \cdots + (2^m - 1) \cdot \binom{n}{n} = (2^m - 1) \cdot 2^n$, which must be the total number of subsets of $A \cup B$. However, this contradicts Theorem 39, which says that $2^{m+n} - 1$ is the number of subsets of $A \cup B$. Where is the error?

4-35. If the order of receipt of the cards is considered, in how many ways can a poker player receive at least one ace in the five cards he is dealt? Only one ace? At least one ace and at least one king? Only one ace and only one king? Two or more aces? Only two aces and only two kings? Two pair? A full house?

4-36. Answer Question 4-35 if the order of receipt of the cards is ignored in each case.

4-37. In Question 4-2, how many members does D have?

4-38. (1) In how many ways can the bridge player Mr. North receive one or more aces in a hand if the order in which he is dealt his thirteen cards is considered? Not considered? (2) Answer these if Mr. North gets only one ace? (3) In how many ways can the fifty-two cards be partitioned into four bridge hands so that Mr. North receives at least three aces and order of dealing is considered? So that some player receives at least three aces and dealing order is considered?

4-39. If the last part of Question 4-38 hasn't driven you sane, try this one. Four alike pennies and six alike dimes are tossed simultaneously and land in a row. How many results are possible? How many results are possible (1) if at least two pennies show heads and (2) if at least two coins show heads? Now answer all these questions if, instead of being alike, the pennies have four different dates, only three of the dimes are dated 1940 and the other dimes have differing dates.

4-40. Expand using the binomial theorem:

$$(p + q)^5 \qquad (3p + q^2)^4 \qquad (a - 2b)^5$$
$$(p + q)^{-4} \qquad (1 + .01)^6 \qquad (.99)^3$$
$$\left(\frac{1}{x + y}\right)^3 \qquad (2a - b)^{-7} \qquad (x^3 - 4)^{\frac{1}{2}}$$

4-41. Compute to the nearest thousandth by using the binomial theorem:

$$(1 + .01)^{20} \qquad (.98)^{18} \qquad (1.02)^{-11} \qquad (.01)^{\frac{1}{2}}$$

4-42. What is the sixth term of the binomial-theorem expansion of $(a + b)^{12}$? Of $(5x^2 - 3)^n$? What is the rth term of $(x + y)^{14}$?

4-43. Observe that if $(x + y)(x + y)(x + y)(x + y)(x + y)$ is multiplied out, the term $x^3 y^2$ (for example) appears $\binom{5}{2}$ times before you simplify your answer by collecting like terms. Now show that the binomial theorem is true for the case in which the exponent is the counting number n.

4-44. Suppose A is a number and B is a number. Show that, if n is a counting number such that

$(A + B)^n$

$$= \binom{n}{0}A^nB^0 + \binom{n}{1}A^{n-1}B^1 + \binom{n}{2}A^{n-2}B^2 + \cdots + \binom{n}{n}A^0B^n$$

is true for n, then

$$(A + B)^{n+1} = \binom{n+1}{0}A^{n+1}B^0 + \binom{n+1}{1}A^nB^1 + \binom{n+1}{2}A^{n-1}B^2$$

$$+ \cdots + \binom{n+1}{n+1}A^0B^{n+1}$$

is true for $n + 1$.

4-45. Use what you showed in Question 4-44, plus the fact that $(A + B)^1$ $= \binom{1}{0}A^1B^0 + \binom{1}{1}A^0B^1$, to explain verbally (use no algebra) why there can be *no* counting number k for which the equation

$$(A + B)^k = \binom{k}{0}A^kB^0 + \binom{k}{1}A^{k-1}B^1 + \cdots + \binom{k}{k}A^0B^k$$

is false. This kind of argument ("If it is true for n then it is true for $n + 1$; it is true for the case where n is 1; therefore it can be false for no counting number") is called *mathematical induction*.

4-46. By a mathematical induction argument, show that if n is a counting number then $1 + 2 + 3 + \cdots + n = \binom{n+1}{2}$.

4-47. If a is a number and r is a number, then the n-term number sequence $a, ar, ar^2, ar^3, \ldots, ar^{n-1}$ is called a *geometric progression*. Use an induction argument to show that the sum of the first n terms is

$$\frac{a - ar^n}{1 - r}.$$

4-48. Compute cautiously and clearly the chances that a certain congruency cropping up continuously in this clause is merely careless coincidence.

chapter five

More Applications and Theorems of Combinatorial Analysis

5-1. SOME PROBABILITY LAWS

Suppose the makers of Guillotine razor blades ("For the shave that's REALLY close!") have blades coming off their production line in lots of 10,000. To insure high quality, exactly 100 blade-inspections are performed on each lot. If exactly 200 of the blades in the most recent lot are actually defective, in how many ways and orders can the inspector sample this lot and reject exactly four times? There are two cases to be considered. Case (1) is sampling with replacement, in which each inspected blade is immediately returned to the lot before making the next selection, so that it is possible to select and inspect the same blade more than once (or even all 100 times). Case (2) is sampling without replacement, in which no blade can be selected more than once. In either case, the four defective inspections can be distributed over the 100 total inspections in exactly $\binom{100}{4}$ possible occupancy patterns, of which XXXXOOOOOO $\cdots$ O and OXOXOXOXOOO $\cdots$ O and OOXXO $\cdots$ OOXOXO are three examples. In case (1), for each of these $\binom{100}{4}$ occupancy patterns, the four defective positions may be filled in from the 200 defective blades available in 200^4 orders (the number of four-term sequences which can be made *with* repetition from a set of 200 things), and for each of these orders, the ninety-six non-defective positions can be filled in from the 9,800 available good blades in 9800^{96} orders. Hence, $\binom{100}{4} \cdot 200^4 \cdot 9800^{96}$ is the answer for case (1). In case (2), in which sampling without replacement occurs, each of the $\binom{100}{4}$ occupancy patterns may have its four defective positions filled in $200^{(4)}$ orders (the number of four-term sequences which can be made from a set of 200 things *without* repetition because, in this case, sampling is *without* replacement), and for each of these orders the ninety-six non-defective positions can be filled in from the available 9,800 good blades in $9800^{(96)}$ orders. Thus, $\binom{100}{4} \cdot 200^{(4)} \cdot 9800^{(96)}$ is the answer for case (2).

Suppose, in the razor blade example, we are also asked to find the probability that exactly four inspections reveal defective blades. For each of the cases (1) and (2), we merely divide the answer previously obtained by No.(S), the total number of significant outcomes. No.(S) would be the total number of ways and orders of drawing the sample of 100 inspections from 10,000 blades. In case (1) No.(S) is 10000^{100} and in case (2) No.(S) is $10000^{(100)}$. So our probabilities are given by

$$\frac{\binom{100}{4} \cdot 200^4 \cdot 9800^{96}}{10000^{100}} \quad \text{and} \quad \frac{\binom{100}{4} \cdot 200^{(4)} \cdot 9800^{(96)}}{10000^{(100)}}$$

in cases (1) and (2) respectively.

As a general rule, *if* we have a set of N members, exactly R of which have a certain property which interests us, and on each of exactly n trials we select (randomly) a member of this N-member set, *then*

$$\frac{\binom{n}{r} \cdot R^r \cdot (N-R)^{n-r}}{N^n} \quad \text{or} \quad \frac{\binom{n}{r} \cdot R^{(r)} \cdot (N-R)^{(n-r)}}{N^{(n)}}$$

gives the probability that, on exactly r of the trials, the member selected has the "interesting" property. The first expression above is for the case in which we select with repetition allowed, while the second expression above applies to selection without repetition. These two expressions are respectively referred to as the *binomial probability law* and the *hypergeometric probability law*.

Observe that $\binom{n}{r} \cdot R^r \cdot (N-R)^{n-r}/N^n$ can be simplified to $\binom{n}{r} \cdot (R/N)^r \cdot$ $(1 - R/N)^{n-r}$, which is the $r + 1$ term of the binomial–theorem expansion for $[(1 - R/N) + (R/N)]^n$. Hence, *each* of the $n + 1$ terms in this binomial expansion is a probability for the number of trials which yield a member with the "interesting" property. (This is why the binomial probability law is so named.) We want the sum of all such probabilities to be 1, because we want the probability that something (significant) will occur to be No.(S)/No.(S), which is 1. Happily, the sum of all the terms is 1, because $[(1 - R/N) + (R/N)]^n$ is 1^n, which is 1.

Observe that $\binom{n}{r} \cdot R^{(r)} \cdot (N-R)^{(n-r)}/N^{(n)}$ is

$$\binom{n}{r} R!(N-R)!(N-n)!/(R-r)![(N-R)-(n-r)]!N!,$$

which is

$$\binom{n}{r} \cdot \frac{(N-n)!}{(R-r)![(N-n)-(R-r)]!} \cdot \frac{1}{N!/R!(N-R)!} \quad \text{or} \quad \frac{\binom{n}{r}\binom{N-n}{R-r}}{\binom{N}{R}}.$$

The probability that *something* will happen when we are drawing n times without repetition is

$$\frac{\binom{n}{0}\binom{N-n}{R-0}}{\binom{N}{R}} + \frac{\binom{n}{1}\binom{N-n}{R-1}}{\binom{N}{R}} + \cdots$$

$$+ \frac{\binom{n}{r}\binom{N-n}{R-r}}{\binom{N}{R}} + \cdots + \frac{\binom{n}{R}\binom{N-n}{R-R}}{\binom{N}{R}}^{*}.$$

We hope this sum is one, because No.(S)/No.(S) is one.

Theorem 44. *If* N, R, n *is a counting-number sequence and* $R \leqq N$ *and* $n \leqq N$, *then*

$$\binom{n}{0}\binom{N-n}{R-0} + \binom{n}{1}\binom{N-n}{R-1} + \binom{n}{2}\binom{N-n}{R-2} + \cdots$$

$$+ \binom{n}{R}\binom{N-n}{R-R} = \binom{N}{R}.$$

---

*It will be seen later, in Section 5–3 of this chapter, that if $R > n$ then each of the coefficients $\binom{n}{R}$, $\binom{n}{R-1}$, $\binom{n}{R-2}$, ..., $\binom{n}{n+1}$ is zero, and if $R > N - n$ then each of the coefficients $\binom{N-n}{R}$, $\binom{N-n}{R-1}$, $\binom{N-n}{R-2}$, ..., $\binom{N-n}{N-n+1}$ is zero. Hence the summation is correct whether $R > n$ or $R < n$ and is correct whether $R > N - n$ or $R < N - n$.

This theorem can be proved with the aid of a certain theorem about polynomials which is stated in a question at the end of this chapter.

The following example is associated with Theorem 44. The Acme Company has N new job openings to be filled, n of which are executive positions. The personnel manager, who realizes that federal law prohibits sex discrimination in the hiring of personnel, feels that exactly R of the N positions should be filled with females. He decides that r of the n executive jobs will go to females and the other $R - r$ females will be in the $N - n$ non-executive jobs. Under these conditions, in how many ways can the sexes be distributed over the N positions if we disregard the order of hiring? To answer this we observe that there are $\binom{n}{r}$ ways in which r females can be assigned to the n executive jobs, and for each of these ways there are $\binom{N-n}{R-r}$ ways in which the other $R - r$ females can be assigned to the other $N - R$ non-executive positions. Hence, our answer is $\binom{n}{r}\binom{N-n}{R-r}$, which happens to be the $r + 1$ term in the summation stated in Theorem 44. Notice that the $\binom{N}{R}$ of Theorem 44 would, in this example, be the total number of ways the R females can be assigned to the N jobs without regard to executive and non-executive positions.

If, in this Acme Company example, we add the condition that p of the $N - n$ non-executives are to be clerks and q of these p clerks are to be female, the answer is $\binom{n}{r}\binom{p}{q}\binom{N-n-p}{R-r-q}$. This is the number of ways we can reserve r of the n executive positions for females, times the number of ways we can reserve q of the p clerk jobs for females, times the number of ways we can reserve $R - r - q$ of the remaining $N - n - p$ jobs for the remaining $R - r - q$ females.

In the Guillotine razor blade example we had a "yes or no" situation, so to speak. That is, each blade was either good or bad. Now let us consider a sampling situation in which the items selected may be classified in more than two ways. Suppose an urn contains 10,000 marbles, of which 200 are red, 1,300 are green, 500 are blue, and the other 8,000 are colorless. In how many ways and orders can we select 100 marbles so that four are red, twenty-six are green, five are blue and sixty-five are colorless? Our reasoning parallels the reasoning for the razor blade example. If selection is with repetition, there will be $\binom{100}{4\ 26\ 5\ 65}$ possible occupancy patterns in which the four colors can be distributed over the 100 trials of the sample, and for each of these the four red positions can be filled from the 200 available red marbles in 200^4 ways, the twenty-six green positions can be filled from the 1,300 available green marbles in 1300^{26} ways, the five blue positions can be filled in 500^5 ways, and the sixty-five colorless positions can be filled in 8000^{65} ways. Then $\begin{pmatrix} 100 \\ 4\ 26\ 5\ 65 \end{pmatrix} \cdot 200^4 \cdot 1300^{26} \cdot 500^5 \cdot 8000^{65}$ gives the total number of ways and orders if repetition is allowed. If we divide this number by 10000^{100}, which is the total number of ways and orders in which we can select a sample of 100 marbles, we get the probability of drawing such a sample, with repetition, of course. This simplifies to $\begin{pmatrix} 100 \\ 4\ 26\ 5\ 65 \end{pmatrix} \cdot (.02)^4 \cdot (.13)^{26} \cdot (.05)^5 \cdot (.80)^{65}$, which is one of the terms in the expansion of $(.02 + .13 + .05 + .80)^{100}$. In general, if we have a set of N things which can be *partitioned* into subsets of R_1 members, R_2 members, R_3 members, $\cdots$, R_i members, and if we select n times with repetition allowed, then

$$\begin{pmatrix} n \\ r_1\ r_2\ r_3\ \cdots\ r_i \end{pmatrix} \cdot \left(\frac{R_1}{N}\right)^{r_1} \cdot \left(\frac{R_2}{N}\right)^{r_2} \cdot \left(\frac{R_3}{N}\right)^{r_3} \cdot \cdots \cdot \left(\frac{R_i}{N}\right)^{r_i}$$

is the probability of obtaining r_1 selections from the R_1-member cell and r_2 selections from the R_2-member cell and $\cdots$ and r_i selections from the R_i-member cell. Note that $r_1 + r_2 + \cdots + r_i = n$ and $R_1 + R_2 + \cdots + R_i = N$. Moreover, this expression is a term of the expansion of

$$\left(\frac{R_1}{N} + \frac{R_2}{N} + \cdots + \frac{R_i}{N}\right)^n,$$

and each term in this expansion is in the form of the above probability. These relationships are referred to as the *multinomial probability law* and the *multinomial theorem*. The *binomial law* and *theorem* are special cases of them.

If we are selecting without repetition, then

$$\begin{pmatrix} n \\ r_1\ r_2\ \cdots\ r_i \end{pmatrix} \cdot \frac{R_1{}^{(r_1)} \cdot R_2{}^{(r_2)} \cdot \cdots \cdot R_i{}^{(r_i)}}{N^{(n)}}$$

gives the probability we seek. For example, the probability of Mr. North receiving three clubs, four spades, and six cards of the red suits in a certain bridge hand is

$$\begin{pmatrix} 13 \\ 3\ 4\ 6 \end{pmatrix} \cdot \frac{13^{(3)} \cdot 13^{(4)} \cdot 26^{(6)}}{52^{(13)}}.$$

Mr. Ivan Numbottom, a rabid television fan, steps into his living room, turns on the "glass eye," and rapidly dials the tuning knob through all seven channels which his TV set can receive. If 21 per cent of all TV program time is devoted to soap operas, 53 per cent is taken up by advertising, and the rest is snow, what is the probability that Ivan finds exactly two soap operas? This reminds us of a situation in which we draw seven times from an urn of balls which contains 21 per cent red balls, 53 per cent green balls, and 26 per cent blue balls, and we want to know the probability that exactly two of the seven draws are red. Notice that we classify the draws in two ways: red and non-red. We would use either the binomial probability law or the hypergeometric probability law, depending on whether TV-channel selection is like drawing with replacement or without replacement. Assuming the percentage of time devoted to soap operas is the same for all seven channels, we ought to use the probability law for which the percentage of red balls in the urn is constant from draw to draw. This means drawing with replacement, so the binomial law is the one we use. Hence, $\binom{7}{2} \cdot (.21)^2 \cdot (.79)^5$ is the answer. Now, what is the probability that Ivan dials two soap operas, four commercials, and one snow screen? The answer is the same as the probability of drawing two red balls, four green balls, and one blue ball from the urn—with repetition allowed, of course. Since we now classify the draws three ways (red, green, and blue) we must use the multinomial probability law. We get $\binom{7}{2\ 4\ 1} \cdot (.21)^2 \cdot (.53)^4 \cdot (.26)^1$ for our answer.

Questions at the end of this chapter introduce two other probability laws: the *negative binomial law* and the *hypergeometric waiting-time law*.

5-2. MULTIPLE OCCUPANCY

Suppose five alike balls fall randomly into a large box. The box is partitioned into three compartments, each roomy enough to hold all five balls. How many distinguishable results are possible? The possible occupancy patterns are as follows.

XXXXX				X	XXX	X
XXXX	X			X	XX	XX
XXXX		X		X	X	XXX
XXX	XX			X		XXXX
XXX	X	X			XXXXX	
XXX		XX			XXXX	X
XX	XXX				XXX	XX
XX	XX	X			XX	XXX
XX	X	XX			X	XXXX
XX		XXX				XXXXX
X	XXXX					

There is a way of viewing this problem which will allow us to apply some technique or formula we have already developed. Try to solve the problem yourself before reading further.

Our perplexity is caused by the fact that we can have more than one ball per compartment. We can convert it to an equivalent situation in which no compartment has more than one ball by increasing the number of compartments to seven. In our imagination we erect a wall immediately to the right of each of the "first" four balls in each occupancy pattern. This converts the above twenty-one occupancy patterns into those below.

```
X|X|X|X|X|            |        X|    X|X|X|    X      |
X|X|X|X|  X           |        X|    X|X|     X|X      |
X|X|X|X|  |        X  |        X|    X|       X|X|X     |
X|X|X|    X|X         |        X|    |        X|X|X|X   |
X|X|X|    X|     X    |        X|             X|X|X|X   |
X|X|X|    |      X|X  |        |X|X|X|X|X|
X|X|      X|X|X       |        |X|X|X|X|  X
X|X|      X|X|    X   |        |X|X|X|    X|X
X|X|      X|      X|X |        |X|X|      X|X|X
X|X|      |       X|X|X |      |X|       X|X|X|X
X|        X|X|X|X     |        |        X|X|X|X|X
```

Now no compartment contains two balls. But we still have the same number of occupancy patterns, and this is what is important. There are $\binom{7}{5}$ occupancy patterns because each represents one way a five-member subset (the five occupied compartments) can be chosen from a seven-member set (all seven compartments). The top number, seven, is accounted for by the fact that we originally had three compartments and then added four, which is one less than the number of balls. Therefore $\binom{3 + (5-1)}{5}$ is a more meaningful form in which to express our answer.

If the problem states that r alike balls fall randomly into an n-compartment box, the answer is $\binom{n + (r-1)}{r}$, according to similar reasoning.

On this type of problem it is my experience that students have trouble deciding which number goes in the bottom of the binomial coefficient. The trouble is easily avoided by thinking of each occupancy pattern as a nondecreasing number sequence. In the five-ball three-compartment problem, for example, the first occupancy pattern can be expressed as 1, 1, 1, 1, 1, because each of the five balls is in compartment one; the second pattern would be 1, 1, 1, 1, 2; the pattern |XX |XX |X | is given by 1, 1, 2, 2, 3; and so on. Observe that each of the twenty-one occupancy patterns is expressed as one and only one five-term nondecreasing number sequence made from the first three counting numbers, and every such sequence corresponds to one and only one of the twenty-one occupancy patterns. Hence $\binom{3 + (5-1)}{5}$ gives the number of five-term nondecreasing sequences which can be made from the first three counting numbers.

Theorem 45. $\left(\dfrac{n + (r - 1)}{r} \right)$ *is the number of r — term nondecreasing sequences which can be made from the first n counting numbers.*

The following problem is easy if you think of each possibility as a nondecreasing sequence. A candy machine vends eight kinds of dime-sized candy packages. A diet crasher with three dimes approaches the machine and, after the customary banging, muttering, and other forms of coaxing, obtains three bars. How many selections are possible? The answer, of course, is either $\left(\dfrac{8 + (3 - 1)}{3} \right)$ or $\left(\dfrac{3 + (8 - 1)}{8} \right)$, but which? Each possible selection can be represented by a three-term nondecreasing sequence (for example, 1, 8, 8 represents the selection of one bar from the first window in the machine and two bars from the last window); therefore the bottom number in the binomial coefficient is three, and our answer is $\left(\dfrac{8 + (3 - 1)}{3} \right)$.

Observe that in these occupancy problems we are not concerned about the order in which the balls fall or the dimes are inserted. For each compartment (or machine window) it is true that, if a ball falls into it (or a candy bar is chosen from it), we do not care which ball it is (or which choice it is). If, instead of r alike balls falling into n compartments, we have r balls numbered from 1 to r falling into n compartments, then the number of possible results would be n^r. Think of the r numbered balls as being like r terms, and think of the n compartments as being like the first n counting numbers from which r-term sequences are made, with repetition allowed.

Suppose the original problem of r alike balls falling randomly into a box of n large compartments had asked for the number of distinguishable results in which each compartment contains at least one ball. For this case $r \geq n$, of course. Since the balls are alike and we do not care which ball it is that a compartment receives, we imagine n of the r balls falling one-to-the-compartment, and this leaves the remaining $r - n$ balls yet to be distributed. The number of results, then, is the number of ways these $r - n$ balls can fall randomly into the n-compartment box. This, as we have seen, is $\left(\dfrac{n + (r - n - 1)}{r - n} \right)$. It simplifies to $\left(\dfrac{r - 1}{r - n} \right)$ or $\left(\dfrac{r - 1}{n - 1} \right)$.

Theorem 46. $\left(\dfrac{n + (r - n - 1)}{r - n} \right)$ *is the number of r-term nondecreasing sequences which can be made from the first n counting numbers if each of the first n counting numbers appears at least once in each sequence. Moreover,* $\left(\dfrac{n + (r - kn - 1)}{r - kn} \right)$ *is the number of r-term nondecreasing sequences which can be made from the first n counting numbers if each of the first n counting numbers appears at least k times in each sequence.*

A glass-globed gum machine which vends colored gum balls contains exactly thirty gum balls, of which exactly six are fiery red-hots and the rest are green. Five children use the machine repeatedly, each one rapidly cramming gum balls into his mouth until he tastes his first red. How many results (i.e., distributions of the balls) are possible? In this problem there are six compartments—namely the five mouths and the glass globe—which together contain thirty balls. Each compartment contains at least one ball because each mouth contains one fiery red hot and there is a sixth red left in the machine. The answer, then, is $\binom{30-1}{6-1}$.

5-3. FUNDAMENTAL DEFINITION AND PROPERTIES OF THE BINOMIAL COEFFICIENT

Mathematicians who work in the branch of mathematics known as *finite differences* use the following very interesting definitions and theorems. *If x is a number* (any number!), *and r is an integer, then let*

$$x^{(r)} \ mean \begin{cases} 0 \ \textit{if r is negative, and} \\ 1 \ \textit{if r is zero, and} \\ x \cdot (x-1) \cdot (x-2) \cdot \ \cdots \ \cdot (x-r+1) \ \textit{if r is positive.} \end{cases}$$

Theorem 47. If r and k are integers such that $0 \leq k \leq r$, *then*

$$(x+1)^{(r)} - (x)^{(r)} = r \cdot x^{(r-1)}, \text{ and}$$
$$x^{(k)} \cdot (x-k)^{(r-k)} = x^{(r)}.$$

Notice that the expression $n^{(r)}$, which we have been using to denote the number of *r*-term sequences which can be made without repetition from the first *n* counting numbers, is the special case of the $x^{(r)}$ definition in which *x* and *r* are both counting numbers and *r* is not greater than *n*.

Theorem 48. If n is a nonnegative integer and so is r, then

$$n^{(r)} = \begin{cases} \dfrac{n!}{(n-r)!} \ \textit{if } n \geq r, \textit{ and} \\ 0 \ \textit{if } n < r. \end{cases}$$

Using $x^{(r)}$, we are able to obtain a more general definition for $\binom{x}{r}$ which applies to cases in which *x* is not an integer. Such binomial coefficients occur in the binomial–theorem expansion of $(A+B)^x$ when *x* is not an integer. *If x is a number, then let*

$$\binom{x}{r} \ mean \begin{cases} x^{(r)}/r! \ \textit{if r is a nonnegative integer, and} \\ 0 \ \textit{if r is a negative integer.} \end{cases}$$

Theorem 49. If x is a number and r is an integer, then

$$\binom{x}{r} = \begin{cases} 0 \ \textit{if } r \textit{ is negative, and} \\ 1 \ \textit{if } r \textit{ is zero, and} \\ \dfrac{x(x-1)(x-2)\cdots(x-r+1)}{1\cdot2\cdot3\cdots\cdot r} \ \textit{if } r \textit{ is positive.} \end{cases}$$

Theorem 50. *If x is a number and r is an integer and k is an integer, then*

$$\binom{x+1}{r} - \binom{x}{r} = \binom{x}{r-1}, \ \textit{and}$$

$$\binom{x}{k}\binom{x-k}{r-k} = \binom{x}{r}\binom{r}{k}, \ \textit{and}$$

if k is a counting number then

$$\binom{x+k}{r} - \binom{x}{r} = \binom{x}{r-1} + \binom{x+1}{r-1}$$
$$+ \binom{x+2}{r-1} + \cdots + \binom{x+k-1}{r-1}.$$

Theorem 51. *If $x > 0$ and r is an integer, then* $\left(\dfrac{-x}{r}\right) = (-1)^r \cdot \binom{x+r-1}{r}.$

Of course, x must be a counting number and r must be a counting number not greater than x in order for $\binom{x}{r}$ to be the number of r-member subsets of an x-member set.

Theorem 52. *If n is a nonnegative integer and r is an integer, then*

$$\binom{n}{r} = \begin{cases} 0 \ \textit{if } r > n, \textit{ and} \\ \dfrac{n!}{r!(n-r)!} \ \textit{if } r \le n, \textit{ and} \end{cases}$$

$$\binom{0}{0} = 1, \ \textit{and}$$

$$\binom{0}{r} = 0 \ \textit{if } r \ne 0, \textit{ and}$$

$$\binom{n}{0} = \binom{n}{n} = 1, \ \textit{and}$$

$$\binom{n}{1} = \binom{n}{n-1} = n, \ \textit{and}$$

$$\binom{n}{r} = \binom{n}{n-r}$$

5-4. PASCAL'S TRIANGLE AND SOME BINOMIAL-COEFFICIENT IDENTITIES

In the seventeenth century the now-famous French mathematician Blaise Pascal constructed this infinite "triangle" of numbers, each of which

$$
\begin{array}{ccccccccccc}
 & & & & & 1 & & & & & \\
 & & & & 1 & & 1 & & & & \\
 & & & 1 & & 2 & & 1 & & & \\
 & & 1 & & 3 & & 3 & & 1 & & \\
 & 1 & & 4 & & 6 & & 4 & & 1 & \\
1 & & 5 & & 10 & & 10 & & 5 & & 1
\end{array}
$$
$$\cdot \quad \cdot \quad \cdot$$

is a binomial coefficient. It is known as *Pascal's Triangle*. For each pair of adjacent numbers in the same row of his triangle, their sum appears immediately below them. Moreover, each binomial coefficient $\binom{n}{r}$, in which n is a nonnegative integer and so is r, appears exactly once. For example, $\binom{4}{2}$ is the 6 in the triangle shown. If we slide each row to the left and write each number as a nonnegative-integer binomial coefficient, as shown, we obtain another form of the triangle which will be more meaningful for our purposes. If n is a nonnegative integer and r is a nonnegative integer, then $\binom{n}{r}$ occupies the position at row n and column r in our version of Pascal's Triangle. For example, the number $\binom{3}{0}$ is in both row three and column zero in our version.

$$
\begin{array}{llllll}
\binom{0}{0} & & & & & \\
\binom{1}{0} & \binom{1}{1} & & & & \\
\binom{2}{0} & \binom{2}{1} & \binom{2}{2} & & & \\
\binom{3}{0} & \binom{3}{1} & \binom{3}{2} & \binom{3}{3} & & \\
\binom{4}{0} & \binom{4}{1} & \binom{4}{2} & \binom{4}{3} & \binom{4}{4} & \\
\binom{5}{0} & \binom{5}{1} & \binom{5}{2} & \binom{5}{3} & \binom{5}{4} & \binom{5}{5}
\end{array}
$$
$$\cdot \quad \cdot \quad \cdot$$

The importance of Pascal's Triangle is that the algebraic relationships between the nonnegative-integer binomial coefficients can be visualized as geometric relationships between "positions" of the triangle. This makes them easier to understand and remember. For example, Theorems 50 to 52 state binomial–coefficient equations, called *identities*, which are relationships between two or more "positions," and are easier to remember against the background of the triangle. Observe that the third part of Theorem 50 adds k consecutive members of the $r-1$ column in the triangle. The sixth part of Theorem 52 shows that each row is "symmetric about its center"—that is, two members of a row which are "equidistant from its center" are equal. For each row of the triangle, the third part of Theorem 53 gives the sum of all the binomial coefficients in that row.

Theorem 53. *If n is a nonnegative integer and r is an integer and k is a counting number, then*

$$\binom{n}{r+1}\cdot(r+1) = \binom{n}{r}\cdot(n-r) \quad and$$

$$\binom{n}{r+k}\cdot(r+k)^{(k)} = \binom{n}{r}\cdot(n-r)^{(k)}, \quad and$$

$$\binom{n}{0} + \binom{n}{1} + \binom{n}{2} + \cdots + \binom{n}{n-1} + \binom{n}{n} = 2^n, \quad and$$

$$\binom{n}{0} - \binom{n}{1} + \binom{n}{2} - \binom{n}{3} + \cdots + (-1)^n\binom{n}{n} = 0, \quad and$$

$$\binom{n}{0} + \binom{n}{2} + \binom{n}{4} + \cdots = \binom{n}{1} + \binom{n}{3} + \binom{n}{5} + \cdots = 2^{n-1}, \quad and$$

$$\binom{n}{0}^2 + \binom{n}{1}^2 + \binom{n}{2}^2 + \cdots + \binom{n}{n}^2 = \binom{2n}{n}.$$

Each identity in Theorem 53 relates triangle positions which are in the same row. (The binomial theorem is often helpful in proving identities relating several consecutive positions which are all in the same row.) In Theorem 44 we have an identity which relates some consecutive members of the n row with some consecutive members of the $N - n$ row.

And now, here are some identities, each of which relates binomial coefficients which are in the same column of Pascal's Triangle.

Theorem 54. *If n is a nonnegative integer and r is an integer and k is a counting number, then* $\binom{n}{r}\cdot(n-r) = \binom{n-1}{r}\cdot n$ *and*

$$\binom{n}{r}\cdot(n-r)^{(k)} = \binom{n-k}{r}\cdot n^{(k)}, \quad and \; if \; r \geqq 0 \; then \; \binom{r}{r} +$$

$$\binom{r+1}{r} + \binom{r+2}{r} + \cdots + \binom{r+k}{r} = \binom{r+k+1}{r+1}, \quad and$$

$$if \; r \geqq 1 \; then \; \binom{r}{r} - \binom{r+1}{r} + \binom{r+2}{r} - \binom{r+3}{r} + \cdots$$
$$= 2^{-r-1}.$$

The third identity in this theorem shows us that a binomial coefficient in the $r + 1$ column can be computed by mere addition if we know all the numbers which are higher than it and in the r column of Pascal's Triangle.

Members on a diagonal of the triangle are related by this next theorem.

Theorem 55. *If n is a nonnegative integer and r is a nonnegative integer not greater than n, then*

$$\binom{n-1}{r} + \binom{n-2}{r-1} + \binom{n-3}{r-2} + \cdots$$
$$+ \binom{n-r-1}{0} = \binom{n}{r}.$$

When you finish proving the identities in the foregoing theorems plus those in the questions which follow, you will have covered the properties of binomial coefficients which are customarily considered to be the fundamental ones. There are hundreds of other binomial-coefficient identities, and proving them can be as much fun as any other kind of puzzle if you are not in a position where you feel forced to succeed within some time limit. It is even said in some quarters that theorem proving is therapeutic—it makes fat people thin and thin people good looking, although my own experience is that it makes good-looking people fat.

Questions

5-1. An urn contains 100 balls, of which 70 are white and the other 30 are red. We draw 20 balls with replacement. In how many distinguishable ways and orders can we get 12 white draws and 8 red draws (1) if all 100 balls are distinguishable from each other, (2) if the reds can be distinguished from each other but the whites are alike, or (3) if the reds are alike and the whites are alike? Now go back and state what the answers would be if we had drawn without replacement.

5-2. In Question 5-1, state the probability number which corresponds to each answer.

5-3. Orestes McGurk is sent to the store for a dozen eggs by his wife, Zsa-Zsa, who claims that he is the world's rottenest egg picker. If exactly ten of the 200 loose eggs in the egg bin at the Gastronomic Galaxie are rotten, what is the probability that Orestes will come home with only eight bad eggs in the dozen this time?

5-4. The noble old firm of Codger, Geezer, and Curmudgeon, Inc., manufacturers of buggy whips, was formerly the crack outfit in the field; but its sales have been steadily declining since 1910. Hard people to discourage, the management has decided to take aggressive, dynamic, forward-looking action *now* (before it is really necessary) and plunge headlong into another product field: horse collars. A vigorous sales campaign will be based upon the latest artistic styling and eye-appeal (appeal to the horse, of course). But the question of color remains to be answered: "Do most horses prefer pimlico-pink to seabiscuit-cerise?" This momentous issue is to be settled by selecting, with repetition, a random sample of ten milk-wagon horses in the town of Boondock Center and asking each one the foregoing question. Now if it is true that exactly 75 per cent of all the 10,000 living harness horses in the U.S. actually would prefer pimlico-pink to seabiscuit-cerise, in how many ways and orders can the pollsters get more than four answers which are nays?

5-5. Prove Theorem 44. You may assume the truth of the following theorem and use it in your argument if you wish. *Theorem.* If a_0, $a_1, a_2, \cdots, a_n$ is a number sequence and $b_0, b_1, b_2, \cdots, b_n$ is a number sequence such that, for each number x, it is true that $a_0 + a_1x + a_2x^2 + \cdots + a_nx^n = b_0 + b_1x + b_2x^2 + \cdots + b_nx^n$; then $a_0 = b_0$ and $a_1 = b_1$ and $a_2 = b_2 \cdots$ and $a_n = b_n$.

5-6. In the Acme Company example (which follows Theorem 44 in the text) we distributed the R females to the "population" of n executive and $N - n$ nonexecutive positions to get an answer of $\binom{n}{r}\binom{N-n}{R-r}$. What answer would have been obtained if, instead, we had distributed the n executive positions to the "population" of R females and $N - R$ males? Although these two answers are not equivalent, you can show that

$$\frac{\binom{n}{r}\binom{N-n}{R-r}}{\binom{N}{R}} = \frac{\binom{R}{r}\binom{N-R}{n-r}}{\binom{N}{n}}.$$

Show it. What is the significance of this? Show that R's and n's can be swapped in Theorem 44.

5-7. In how many ways and orders can you draw three red, two yellow, and five green balls from an urn containing twenty unlike red balls, eight unlike yellow balls, and twelve unlike green balls (1) with repetition, (2) without repetition? What is the probability of drawing three red, two yellow, and five green in each case?

5-8. SIMP, the Society for an Insane Military Policy, which advocates burning the world to a blackened cinder in a nuclear holocaust, has only thirty members. Of these, fourteen joined because they want to teach the enemy a lesson he will never forget, another seven see this as a complete solution to the problem of jaywalking, and the remaining nine members are merely party-goers who enjoy a real blast now and then. If ten members are selected at random to carry posters in a Bang the Bomb march, what is the probability that five of these ten are "teachers," two are anti-jaywalkers, and three are party-goers?

5-9. If ten dice are tossed simultaneously, what is the probability that only three of them will show a score of five? That none will show a five?

5–10. A jet fighter is armed with the Orange Orangutan air-to-air missile, which scores a hit 30 per cent of the time. If the plane fires a salvo of five from a pod, what is the probability of exactly one hit? Of exactly three hits? Of at least one hit?

5–11. Suppose that 1 per cent of the time the Orange Orangutan missile of Question 5–10 will be a hang-fire which remains in the pod. What is the probability that, if ten missiles are fired (two salvos from different pods), exactly three will score hits, six will fire and miss, and one will be a hang-fire?

5–12. In the expansion of $(a + b + c + d)^9$, after like terms have been collected, what is the multinomial coefficient of the a^3bc^4d term? Of the a^5bd^3 term? What is the sum of all the multinomial coefficients?

5–13. If nineteen dice are tossed simultaneously, in how many ways can this result in three ones, six twos, no threes, two fours, five fives, and three sixes?

5–14. *Negative Binomial Probability Law.* We have an urn containing exactly N balls, of which R are red and $N - R$ are green. We continue drawing with repetition and examining balls until we get our r^{th} red draw. Show that if k is zero or a counting number, then the number of ways and orders in which the rth red draw can occur on the $(r + k)^{\text{th}}$ draw is $\binom{r + k - 1}{r - 1} R^r (N - R)^k$ and the probability is $\binom{r + k - 1}{r - 1}\left(\frac{R}{N}\right)^r\left(1 - \frac{R}{N}\right)^k$, if drawing is with repetition.

5–15. *Hypergeometric Waiting Time Probability Law.* Show that the results would have been

$$\binom{r + k - 1}{r - 1} R^{(r)}(N - R)^{(k)} \text{ and } \frac{\binom{r + k - 1}{r - 1}\binom{N - (r + k)}{R - r}}{\binom{N}{R}}$$

respectively, in the preceding question if drawing had been without repetition.

5–16. Show that if the *probability* expressions given in Questions 5–14 and 5–15 are each multiplied by $\frac{r + k}{r}$, the results are the probabilities of getting r red draws in $r + k$ draws, with repetition and without repetition, respectively.

5–17. If r is a counting number, show that the negatively exponented binomial $\left[\frac{N}{R} + \left(1 - \frac{N}{R}\right)\right]^{-r}$ is equal to

$$\binom{r+0-1}{r-1}\left(\frac{R}{N}\right)^r\left(1-\frac{R}{N}\right)^0 + \binom{r+1-1}{r-1}\left(\frac{R}{N}\right)^r\left(1-\frac{R}{N}\right)^1$$
$$+ \binom{r+2-1}{r-1}\left(\frac{R}{N}\right)^r\left(1-\frac{R}{N}\right)^2 + \cdots.$$

Observe that each term in the summation is a negative-binomial-law probability, and this is why the law is so named. Notice also that the sum of all the terms is 1, because $\left[\frac{N}{R}+\left(1-\frac{N}{R}\right)\right]^{-r} = 1$. Interpret the significance of this in terms of probabilities and No.(S).

5-18. We continue drawing from a deck of playing cards until the third time we draw a heart. What is the probability that we will stop drawing on the tenth draw if we are drawing (1) with replacement, and (2) without replacement.

5-19. Clem Clump, the world's clumsiest mortal, claims he was attacked by a folding beach chair last Saturday at Pismo Beach. In a nasty letter to the Collapsable Chair Co., Clem opined that if there is even one such monster in a thousand beach chairs, the manufacturers should be drawn and quartered and also required to find the carnivorous chair and keep it off the market (preferably by using it themselves). Anxious to please, the company decides to examine carefully (without repetition) every one of the 5,000 chairs coming off its production line this month. If, on the average, 3 chairs out of 1,000 made by the company are vicious, what is the probability that the first bad one will be (1) the hundredth one examined and (2) among the first 100 examined? (3) What is the probability that the fifth defective found will be the 2,000th chair examined?

5-20. Answer the preceding question if sampling is with repetition.

5-21. Show that the expression for the hypergeometric-waiting-time probability given in Question 5-15 is equal to

$$\frac{r}{r+k}\cdot\frac{\binom{R}{r}\binom{N-R}{k}}{\binom{N}{r+k}},$$

which is the same as $r/(r+k)$, or r/n, times the hypergeometric probability for what experiment?

5-22. A filing cabinet drawer has twenty-six folders, one for each letter of the alphabet. In how many ways can 100 documents be filed if, for each folder, the order of its contents is ignored? Now answer if you are told that each folder holds at least one of the 100 documents? At least two of the 100 documents?

5-23. In how many distinguishable ways can five patrons of Bucky's Cafe de la Cuisine Magnifique (of Question 4–11) each order only one item from the à la carte menu if the patrons are identical quintuplets?

5-24. How many multinomial coefficients are there of the form $\left(\begin{smallmatrix} 15 \\ a\ b\ c \end{smallmatrix}\right)$? How many ten-term number sequences can be made with repetition from the lowest twenty-four nonnegative integers such that, in each sequence, the sum of the ten terms is twenty-three?

5-25. Instead of $\left(\begin{smallmatrix} n+r-1 \\ r \end{smallmatrix}\right)$, why did we not get $n^r/r!$ for the number of distinguishable ways in which r alike balls can occupy an n-compartment box? After all, we do allow repetition in that a box may be "chosen" by more than one ball!

5-26. In how many ways can a telephone repairman carry an (unordered) inventory of thirteen phones in his truck if the telephone company has four styles of telephone to offer: the old-style cradle phone, the wall phone, the princess phone, and the Austro-Hungarian Archduke? What is the answer if he must carry at least two of each type of phone?

5-27. In the beginning of Section 5–2 of this chapter are listed twenty-one occupancy patterns, each showing five X's and four vertical box "walls." If we ignore the extreme left wall and the extreme right wall, each occupancy pattern can be represented as a seven–term sequence made from five alike X's and two alike walls. How can Theorem 40 be applied to obtain the $\left(\begin{smallmatrix} 5+(3-1) \\ 5 \end{smallmatrix}\right)$ answer?

5-28. If n is a counting number and so is r, show that $\left(\begin{smallmatrix} n+r-1 \\ r \end{smallmatrix}\right)$ is equal to

$$\binom{n}{1}\binom{r-1}{1-1} + \binom{n}{2}\binom{r-1}{2-1} + \binom{n}{3}\binom{r-1}{3-1} + \cdots$$
$$+ \binom{n}{n-1}\binom{r-1}{n-1-1} + \binom{n}{n}\binom{r-1}{n-1}.$$

Interpret this in terms of r alike balls dropping into an n–compartment box.

5-29. Reread the last part of Section 5–2 of this chapter, in which the $\left(\begin{smallmatrix} r-1 \\ n-1 \end{smallmatrix}\right)$ expression is obtained. In the light of this, reinterpret the negative-binomial-law coefficients $\left(\begin{smallmatrix} r+k-1 \\ r-1 \end{smallmatrix}\right)$, which are in the same form as the $\left(\begin{smallmatrix} r-1 \\ n-1 \end{smallmatrix}\right)$ of Theorem 46.

5–30. An urn contains exactly 100 balls, of which 70 are white and 30 are red. We draw 20 times with replacement. If order of drawing is considered, how many distinguishable results are possible (1) if all balls are distinguishable from each other, (2) if the reds are distinguishable from each other but the whites are alike, and (3) if the whites are alike and the reds are alike? Simplify each answer as much as possible. Now go back and give answers if we draw without replacement.

5–31. Evaluate: $8^{(5)}$, $2^{(5)}$, $(-7)^{(5)}$, $5^{(-2)}$, $3^{(0)}$, $9^{(6)} - 8^{(6)}$, $\binom{8}{5}$, $\binom{2}{5}$, $\binom{-7}{5}$, $\binom{5}{-2}$, $\binom{3}{0}$, $\binom{\frac{1}{2}}{4}$, $\binom{-2}{6}$, $\binom{-1}{r}$, $\binom{-2}{2r}$, $\binom{3.14}{3}$, $\binom{-3.14}{3}$, $\binom{9.14}{4} - \binom{4.14}{4}$.

5–32. Show that if r is an integer and k is an integer and $0 \leq k \leq r$ and x is a number, then

$$(x + k - 1)^{(r-1)} + (x + k - 2)^{(r-1)} + \cdots$$
$$+ (x + 1)^{(r-1)} + x^{(r-1)} = \frac{(x + k)^{(r)}}{r} - \frac{x^{(r)}}{r}.$$

5–33. Show that if r is a counting number, then $\left[\frac{N}{R} + \left(1 - \frac{N}{R}\right)\right]^{-r}$ is also equal to

$$\binom{-r + 1}{0}\left(\frac{N}{R}\right)^{-r} + \binom{-r}{1}\left(\frac{N}{R}\right)^{-r-1}\left(1 - \frac{N}{R}\right)$$
$$+ \binom{-r - 1}{2}\left(\frac{N}{R}\right)^{-r-2}\left(1 - \frac{N}{R}\right)^{2}$$
$$+ \binom{-r - 2}{3}\left(\frac{N}{R}\right)^{-r-3}\left(1 - \frac{N}{R}\right)^{3} + \cdots.$$

5–34. Are the conclusions of Theorem 47 also true under the alternate hypothesis that r and k are integers such that $r < 0 \leq k$? Which of the conclusions of Theorems 48 to 55 are also true under alternate conditions on r, k, and n?

5–35. Show that if n is a counting number, then

$$2\binom{n}{1} + 4\binom{n}{2} + 6\binom{n}{3} + \cdots + (2n - 2)\binom{n}{n - 1} + 2n\binom{n}{n} = n \cdot 2^n.$$

5–36. Show that if n is a counting number, then

$$\binom{n}{1}AB^{n-1} + 2\binom{n}{2}A^2B^{n-2} + 3\binom{n}{3}A^3B^{n-3} + \cdots$$
$$+ n\binom{n}{n}A^nB^{n-n} = An \cdot (A + B)^{n-1}.$$

5-37. Construct a "psuedo Pascal's Triangle" in which, if n is a nonnegative integer and so is r, then the number $n^{(r)}$ is in the n row and the r column. Now find as many geometric relationships as you can between the positions in the "psuedo triangle" which can be expressed as identities. Compare these identities with corresponding binomial-coefficient identities.

Bibliography

Burford, Roger L. *Introduction to Finite Probability*. Columbus, Ohio: Charles E. Merrill Publishing Company, 1967. 160 pp.

Cangelosi, Vincent E. *Compound Statements and Mathematical Logic*. Columbus, Ohio: Charles E. Merrill Publishing Company, 1967. 128 pp.

Dean, Burton V., Maurice W. Sasieni, Shiv K. Gupta. *Mathematics for Modern Management*. New York and London: John Wiley and Sons, Inc., 1963. 442 pp.

Feller, William. *An Introduction to Probability Theory and Its Applications*. 2nd ed. New York, London, and Sydney: John Wiley and Sons, Inc., 1957. Vol. I, 461 pp.

Freund, John E. *Mathematical Statistics*. Englewood Cliffs, N.J.: Prentice-Hall, Inc., 1962. 390 pp.

Gnedenko, B.V. *Theory of Probability*. Translated from the Russian by B. D. Sekler. New York: Chelsea Publishing Co., 1962.

Goldberg, Samuel. *Probability, An Introduction*. Englewood Cliffs, N.J.: Prentice-Hall, Inc., 1960. 322 pp.

Good, R. A. *Introduction to Mathematics*. New York: Harcourt, Brace & World, Inc., 1966. 545 pp.

Halmos, Paul R. *Naive Set Theory*. Princeton, Toronto, New York, and London: D. Van Nostrand Co., Inc., 1960. 104 pp.

Hart, William L. *Algebra, Elementary Functions, and Probability*. Boston: D. C. Heath & Company, 1965. 547 pp.

Kamke, E. *Theory of Sets*. Translated by Frederick Bagemihl. New York: Dover Publications, Inc., 1950. 144 pp.

Kemeny, John G., Arthur Schleifer, J. Laurie Snell, and Gerald L. Thompson. *Finite Mathematics with Business Applications*. Englewood Cliffs, N.J.: Prentice-Hall, Inc., 1962. 482 pp.

Kolmogorov, A. N. *Foundations of the Theory of Probability.* A translation of the monograph "Grundbegriffe der Wahrscheinlichkeitsre-
chnung," 1933. New York: Chelsea Publishing Co., 1950. 71 pp.

Loève, Michel. *Probability Theory.* 3rd ed. Princeton, N.J.: D. Van
Nostrand Co., Inc., 1963. 685 pp.

Mancill, Julian D. and Mario O. Gonzalez. *Contemporary Mathematics.*
Boston: Allyn & Bacon, Inc., 1966. 590 pp.

Papoulis, Athanasios. *Probability, Random Variables, and Stochastic
Processes.* New York: McGraw-Hill Book Company, 1965. 583 pp.

Parzen, Emanuel. *Modern Probability Theory and Its Applications.* New
York and London: John Wiley and Sons, Inc., 1960. 464 pp.

Pfeiffer, Paul E. *Concepts of Probability Theory.* New York: McGraw-
Hill Book Company, 1965. 399 pp.

Sominskii, I. S. *The Method of Mathematical Induction.* Translated from
the Russian by Halina Moss. Popular Lectures in Mathematics
Series, Vol. I. New York and London: Blaisdell Publishing Co.,
1961. 57 pp.

Suppes, Patrick. *Axiomatic Set Theory.* Princeton, N.J.: D. Van Nostrand
Co., Inc., 1960. 265 pp.

Index

107